P9-ELI-854

Surya
Namaskara
A Technique
of
Solar Vitalization

Nataraj Books
7073-75 Brookfield Plaza
Springfield, VA 22150
Phone (703) 455-4996

Surya Namaskara

A Technique of Solar Vitalization

Swami Satyananda Saraswati

Bihar School of Yoga, Munger, Bihar, India

First published 1973
Reprinted 1976
Second revised & enlarged edition 1983
Third edition 1996
Reprinted 1999

© **1973, 1996**

Copyright reserved by Bihar School of Yoga.

Publisher: Swami Satyasangananda Saraswati,
Honorary Secretary, Bihar School of Yoga,
Ganga Darshan, Munger, Bihar, India.

Printer: Bhargava Bhushan Press, Trilochan,
Varanasi, UP, India.

ISBN: 81-85787-35-2

All rights reserved. No part of this publication may be reproduced, transmitted or stored in a retrieval system, in any form or by any means, without permission in writing from Bihar School of Yoga.

SWAMI SIVANANDA SARASWATI

Swami Sivananda was born at Patta-
madai, Tamil Nadu, in 1887. After
serving as a medical doctor in Malaya,
he renounced his practice, went to
Rishikesh and was initiated into
Dashnami Sannyasa in 1924 by Swami
Vishwananda Saraswati. He toured
extensively throughout India, inspir-
ing people to practise yoga and lead
a divine life. He founded the Divine
Life Society at Rishikesh in 1936, the
Sivananda Ayurvedic Pharmacy in
1945, the Yoga Vedanta Forest

Academy in 1948 and the Sivananda Eye Hospital in 1957.
During his lifetime he guided thousands of disciples and
aspirants all over the world and authored over 200 books.

SWAMI SATYANANDA SARASWATI

Swami Satyananda was born at
Almora, Uttar Pradesh, in 1923. In
1943 he met Swami Sivananda in
Rishikesh and adopted the Dashnami
Sannyasa way of life. In 1955 he left
his guru's ashram to live as a wander-
ing mendicant and later founded the
International Yoga Fellowship in 1963
and the Bihar School of Yoga in 1964.
Over the next 20 years he toured inter-
nationally and authored over 80
books. In 1987 he founded Sivananda
Math, a charitable institution for rural
development, and the Yoga Research Foundation. In 1988
he renounced his mission, adopting kshetra sannyasa, and
now lives as a paramahamsa sannyasin.

SWAMI NIRANJANANANDA SARASWATI

Swami Niranjanananda was born at Rajnandgaon, Madhya Pradesh in 1960. At the age of 4 he joined the Bihar School of Yoga and was initiated into Dashnami Sannyasa at the age of 10. From 1971 he travelled overseas and toured many countries for the next 11 years. In 1983 he was recalled to India and appointed President of Bihar School of Yoga. During the following 11 years he guided the development of Ganga Darshan, Sivananda Math and the Yoga Research Foundation. In 1990 he was initiated as a Paramahamsa and in 1993 anointed Preceptor in succession to Swami Satyananda. Bihar Yoga Bharati was founded under his direction in 1994. He has authored over 20 books and guides national and international yoga programs.

Contents

Contents

Introduction

Surya namaskara is a well known and vital technique within the yogic repertoire. Its versatility and application make it one of the most useful methods to induce a healthy, vigorous and active life and at the same time prepare for spiritual awakening and the resultant expansion of awareness.

In recent years more and more people have moved away from mere ritual and are turning to yoga as a method for exploring and improving their inner lives. Though the need for techniques to enhance physical, mental and spiritual evolution has been recognized, the fast pace of modern living makes it difficult for even the most determined individual to implement yoga practice. And it is practice which is the most important and fundamental issue in terms of our betterment. It is with these thoughts in mind that this book has been written, for surya namaskara is almost a complete sadhana in itself, containing asana, pranayama and meditational techniques within the main structure of the practice.

For most of us, today's lifestyle accentuates mental tensions, worries and seemingly insoluble problems at many levels, such as personal interrelationships, economics, and even geopolitical threats of war and destruction. At the same time the amount of sedentary or semi-sedentary work is increasing due to the increase in technology and labour saving devices. This has led to a situation in which mental and physical ill

1

health is increasing. Without an antidote, there seems to be little hope.

Yoga practices are an ideal antidote to stress and are proving to be the basis of a powerful therapy for mental and physical diseases. Surya namaskara is an integral part of the yogic approach and can be easily integrated into our daily lives for it requires only 5 to 15 minutes of practice daily to obtain remarkably fast and beneficial results. It is therefore ideal for even the most active individuals, such as the busy business-man, the housewife with a family to feed and manage, the student who is facing examinations, or the scientist who spends most of his day thinking.

This book is intended for all persons interested in self-improvement. However, it must be remembered that it is only intended as a guidepost. The main message we wish to impart is the importance of getting down to a daily routine and thereby discovering the effectiveness of this ancient technique through your own effort. You may have read that the practice of surya namaskara revitalizes the body and mind, and helps to eradicate disease, but you must practise the technique in order to find out the truth for yourself.

As we begin to study and perform this series of asana with pranayama, chakra awareness and mantra repetition, we find that few other exercises can match it for completeness. Surya namaskara is more than just a series of physical exercises, though of course it stretches, massages, tones and stimulates all the muscles, vital organs and physical parts by alternatively flexing the body backwards and forwards. It also has a depth and completeness as a spiritual practice.

Surya namaskara is a practice which has been handed down from the sages of vedic times. *Surya* means 'sun' and *namaskara* means 'salutation'. In ancient times the sun was worshipped as a daily ritual because it is a powerful symbol of spiritual consciousness. Worship of the outer and inner sun was a religio-social ritual which attempted to placate those forces of nature beyond man's control. It was initiated by enlightened sages who knew that these practices maintained health and led to greater social creativity and productivity.

2

Surya namaskara is composed of the three elements of form, energy and rhythm. The twelve postures create the physical matrix around which the form of the practice is woven. These postures generate prana, subtle energy, which activates the psychic body. Their performance in a steady, rhythmic sequence reflects the rhythms of the universe, such as the twenty four hours of the day, the twelve zodic phases of the year, the biorhythms of our own body. The rhythmic superimposition of this form and energy on our present body/mind complex is the transforming force which generates the nucleus of a fuller and more active life and a greater appreciation of the richness of the world we live in. Try it for yourself and see.

The Solar Tradition

Surya namaskara is a practice whose origins date far back to the earliest epochs of history, when man first became aware of a spiritual power within himself, reflected in the material universe. This awareness is the foundation of yoga. Surya namaskara, meaning 'salutation to the sun', can be seen as a form of worship of the sun, and all that it represents on the micro and macrocosmic levels. In yogic terms this indicates that the practice of surya namaskara awakens the solar aspects of man's nature and releases this vital energy for the development of higher awareness. This can be realized by the practice of surya namaskara each morning as well as being a fine way to pay tribute to the source of creation and life, thereby carrying on the solar tradition.

Sun worship in the vedic tradition

Adoration and worship of the sun was one of man's first and most natural forms of inner expression. Most of the ancient traditions included some form of sun worship, incorporating various solar symbols and deities, but nowhere have these traditions been as well preserved as they are in the vedic culture. In fact, sun worship is still practised as a daily ritual in many parts of India today.

In ancient India the great avatar Rama became the king of the solar race in the Ramayana. The roots of the present

4

Hindu culture lie in the ancient vedic scriptures, which contain numerous slokas referring to the sun. The Rig Veda itself has many such references, a few of which have been given below:

"Aloft this all wise shining God,
His beams of light are bearing now
That everyone the Sun may see.

Thou goes across the sky's broad place
Meeting the days with rays, O Sun,
And watching generations pass.

The steeds are seven that at thy car
Bear up the God whose hair is flame
O, shining God, O Sun far seen."

Again the seers of the Rig Veda described the sun as:

"The remover of all weakness,
Healer of all illness,
Lord of all that stands and goes.
He slays the demons
And guards the worshippers."

Finally they state:

"We meditate in the adorable glory
of the radiant sun.
May he inspire our intelligence."

The Suryopanishad states that persons who worship the sun as Brahman, become powerful, active, intelligent, and acquire long life. The sun is personified as brilliant like gold, having four arms, seated on a red lotus and riding in a chariot drawn by four horses. He sets in motion the wheels of time, and from him emerge the five physical elements of earth, water, fire, air and ether, as well as the five senses. The

5

Akshyopanishad identifies Surya with Purusha who assumes the form of the sun with thousands of rays, and shines for the good of humanity. There is a verse from the Brihadaranyaka Upanishad which reads as follows:

"O Lord and essence of light
Lead me from the unreal to the real
From the darkness to light
From death to immortality."

Ancient architectural marvels

Several sects of sun worshippers still exist today. Some worship the rising sun, some the setting sun, some the noonday sun. Though these people appear to worship the physical sun, the real object of their worship is Brahman, the Absolute, and its manifestation as creator, preserver, and destroyer, of which the sun is but a symbol.

There are many ancient sun temples existing in India today, some of which date back as far as the 8th century AD, and are architectural marvels. The most famous of these was built at Konark, Orissa, during the 13th century AD. The other main sun temples are located in Kashmir, Gujarat and Andhra Pradesh.

The sun worshippers of ancient India also developed a scientific analysis of the solar system. The Suryasiddhanta is an ancient text on astronomy, dealing with the measurement of time, planetary motions, eclipses and equinoxes.

Ancient history in other traditions is full of numerous references to sun worship. The pyramids, sculptures and inscriptions, which still remain today, indicate that these ancient cultures had a very precise knowledge of the movements of the sun, moon and planets which formed a vital part of both the social and religious affairs. Many of these structures are believed to have been temples, observatories, or both, as no differentiation was made in ancient times between religion and science as it is today. Therefore, we can understand how scientific observations of the sun could also be a part of ritual worship and ceremony.

The Egyptians who followed a complicated form of sun worship, used their knowledge to construct pyramids for interring and preserving the bodies of the pharaohs, so that these sacred heads of state would be able to share the sun's eternal life. The pyramids themselves were symbols of the sun, and were aligned to receive maximum solar radiation.

The Aztec, Inca and Mayan civilizations all had elaborate temples dedicated to the solar gods. The Mayan calendar is said to be one of the most accurate ever produced, revealing detailed knowledge of the sun-thousands of years ago.

Legends of Atlantis, which predate history, indicate that sun worship was practised in those times and that these people condensed solar energy by the use of huge crystals to power cities and transportation systems.

Stonehenge, in Britain, is believed to have been used as a solar observatory to predict the coming of the seasons, solstices and equinoxes, and is also thought to have been a temple of some kind. It is sophisticated far beyond that expected of the primitive tribes previously associated with those times.

The North American Indians lived life by the rhythmic cycle of the sun and seasons. They worshipped the sun, and the basis of many of their beliefs, rituals, construction methods, and so on was a circle or mandala, which symbolized the sun's passage across the sky.

Yang and yin of ancient Chinese philosophy represent the dual relationship existent in nature, symbolized by the sun and moon, or pingala and ida of yogic philosophy.

Modern observations

With the passing of the old cultures and religions, sun worship has lost its significance. Science has become a separate development often replacing religion as the foundation of our beliefs. However, science is now revealing some new and vital information on the sun's activities, which gives us a new understanding of man's relationship with the center of his planetary system.

The sun's surface periodically erupts into huge flares which extend thousands of miles into space and, to us on

7

earth, appear as 'spots' on its surface. These sunspots have been observed to undergo various cycles of increasing and decreasing activity, the main cycle of which is approximately eleven years. Correlations have shown that periods of increased sunspot activity correspond with terrestrial phenomena. There is evidence that wars, revolutions, and migrations often correspond to periods of intense sunspot activity.

The American Foundation for the Study of Cycles has found over 1300 phenomena related to sunspot cycles. These include the increased frequency of auroras, comets, earthquakes, volcanic eruptions, meteor showers, changes in germ cell maturation, electrical potential of trees, fashion, voting trends, fluctuations in stock market prices, increase in the incidence of high blood pressure and diabetes, and many other seemingly unrelated events. This is not surprising when we visualize the immense power of the sun and its radiations, or realize that the earth is constantly being baked in a solar wind. The sun is an integral part of life on earth.

Surya namaskara takes on a new dimension when we become aware of the effects of the sun on our lives, we can then understand how important it was to our ancestors. At the same time, by awakening our own inherent solar forces through this integrated practice, we can attune ourselves to the cosmic nature and revitalize our lives.

Salute to the Sun

Surya namaskara is a series of twelve physical postures. These alternating backward and forward bending asanas flex and stretch the spinal column and limbs through their maximum range. The series gives such a profound stretch to the whole of the body that few other forms of exercise can be compared with it.

Most beginners will discover stiffness in their bodies from muscular tension, tightness in the tendons, and toxic deposits in the joints. Stiffness, lack of coordination, and the tendency to strain, can all be overcome through practising very slowly, with emphasis on awareness and relaxation in each posture. What little physical effort is applied, then appears effortless. Regular practise of surya namaskara is one of the most rapid methods of obtaining a supple body.

The practice should be mastered by first becoming familiar with the postures individually and then as a whole. Synchronizing the breath with the movements is the next step. When this is achieved, it will be found that the breathing sequence complements the postures, and to breathe in any other manner would be awkward and difficult. The basic breathing principle followed is inhalation during backward bending postures, due to expansion of the chest, and exhalation with forward bending postures, due to compression of the chest and abdomen.

9

Before the practice

Before commencing the practice, stand with the feet together, or slightly apart, arms relaxed by your side. Close your eyes and become aware of the whole physical body.

Develop awareness of your body as you would in the practice of yoga nidra. Starting at the top of the head work your awareness down through the body, relaxing any tensions you find on the way. The awareness is like a torchlight piercing into the darkness of the body. Then develop whole body awareness again. Ask yourself, 'How do I feel in relation to my body? Am I relaxed, comfortable with myself?' Then adjust your position so that you are more comfortable with yourself. Feel that you are being pulled upwards by a rope attached to the top of your head.

Now, take your awareness to the bottom of your feet and feel the soles in contact with the floor. Feel that your whole body is being pulled downwards by gravity and that all the tensions from the top of your head are being pulled down through your feet and into the ground. At the same time be aware of the vital force moving up through your body, allowing you to maintain a relaxed and comfortable upright position. Be aware of this for a few moments and then go on to the practice of surya namaskara. Inhale deeply.

THE TWELVE POSTURES

Position 1: Pranamasana or 'prayer pose'

Stand erect with the feet together or slightly apart. Place both palms together in front of the chest (namaskara mudra) and exhale fully. Maintain your awareness on the mudra, the pressure of the palms and the effect of this mudra on the chest area.

Position 2: Hasta Uttanasana or 'raised arms pose'

Raise and stretch both arms above the head, with palms facing upwards. Arch the back and stretch the whole body. Inhale while moving into position. Stretch the head as far back as is comfortably possible and be aware of the curve of the upper back.

Position 3: Padahastasana or 'hand to foot pose'

In a continuous movement, bend forward from the hips. Bring the hands to the floor on either side of the feet and the head as close as possible to the kness. The legs should remain straight. The breath is exhaled while moving into position. Try to keep the back straight, focusing your awareness at the pelvis, the pivoting point for the stretch of the back and leg muscles.

Position 4: Ashwa sanchalanasana or 'the equestrian pose'

Keeping both hands in place, on either side of the feet, bend the left knee while extending the right leg backwards as far as possible. The right toes and knee touch the floor. Bring

13

the pelvis forward, arch the spine and look up. The fingertips touch the floor and balance the body. The breath is inhaled while bringing the chest forward and up. Focus your awareness at the eyebrow center. You should feel the stretch from the thigh moving upward along the front of the body all the way to the eyebrow center.

Position 5: Parvatasana or 'mountain pose'

Bring the left foot back and place it beside the right. Simultaneously raise the buttocks and lower the head between the arms, so that the body forms a triangle with the floor. This movement is performed on exhalation. Aim to put the heels on the floor. Bend the head as far forward as possible so that the eyes are looking at the knees. Focus your awareness at the neck area.

Position 6: Ashtanganamaskara or 'salutation with eight limbs'

Bend the knees to the floor and then bring the chest and chin to the floor, keeping the buttocks elevated. The hands, chin, chest, knees and toes touch the floor, and the spine is arched. The breath is retained in exhalation from position 5.

14

This is the only time that the alternate inhalation and exhalation of the breath is changed. Focus the awareness at the centre of the body or at the back muscles.

Position 7: Bhujangasana or 'serpent pose'

Lower the hips while pushing the chest forward and upward with the arms, until the spine is fully arched and the head is facing up. The legs and lower abdomen remain on the floor and the arms support the trunk. The breath is inhaled while moving forward and upward into position. Focus the awareness at the base of the spine feeling the tension from the forward pull.

Position 8: Parvatasana or 'mountain pose'

Keep the arms and legs straight. While pivoting from the shoulders, raise the buttocks and bring the head down to reassume position 5. Exhale while moving into position.

Position 9: Ashwa sanchalanasana or 'equestrian pose'

Bring the left leg forward, placing the foot between the hands. Simultaneously bring the right knee down to the floor and push the pelvis forward. Arch the spine and look up to reassume position 4. The breath is inhaled while moving into the pose.

Position 10: Padahastasana or 'hand to foot pose'

Bring the right foot in beside the left. Straightening the legs, bend forward and raise the buttocks while bringing the head in towards the knees. The hands remain on the floor beside the feet. This is the same as position 3. Exhale while moving into position.

16

Position 11: Hasta uttanasana or 'raised arms pose'

Raise the torso, stretching the arms above the head. Arch backwards to reassume position 2. Inhale moving into position.

Position 12: Pranamasana or 'prayer pose'

Straighten the body and bring the hands together in front of the chest, reassuming position 1. The breath is exhaled.

Note : This constitutes half a round of surya namaskara. To complete the other half, the same movements are performed, the only variation being that the left leg is brought back in position 4, and the right leg moved forward in position 9. So, one full round consists of 24 movements, 2 sets of 12, giving a balance to each side of the body in each half round. When position 12 is completed, inhale while lowering the hands to the side and then commence the second half of the practice with exhalation.

One full round consists of 24 asanas. In an ideal situation these should be performed in a continuous unbroken flow and, except for ashtanganamaskara, each asana should change with each breath. Of course, if you tire within the round, rest after 12 postures by taking a full breath, inhalation, exhalation and inhalation, before commencing the second half. Take more breaths if you need to. The same thing applies to each individual asana and between rounds. Use the time to reorientate your awareness and posture. Ask yourself, 'How do I feel?', and adjust so that you are comfortable, ensuring that the breath is slow and relaxed before you go on.

Hints and Guidelines

There are several points to keep in mind while practising surya namaskara. These are the keys to successful practice.

Probably, the most important point is to avoid strain. Each movement should be performed with minimum of effort, using only those muscles required to assume and maintain the posture. The rest of the body should remain as relaxed as possible. Relax into each position. In this way your stretching will be more efficient and enjoyable and you will conserve energy. Try to make the movements flow loosely into one another, like a dance.

Surya namaskara involves alternate flexing of the spinal column backwards and forwards. Remember that the neck is also a part of the spine and should be stretched to a comfortable limit backwards and forwards according to the asana. This affords maximum stretch to the body in each position.

Specific hints

1. When learning surya namaskara it is often difficult to place each piece of the jigsaw together. To overcome this, learn the asana one by one in the initial stage. As most people find the transition from positions 3 to 4 difficult, it is wise to piece the series together in two stages. The first stage involves repeating only positions 1, 2, 3, 10, 11, 12. The second stage involves repeating positions 4, 5, 6, 7, 8, 9. Once these two

stages are understood and mastered, they can be easily joined and the total flow of the practice more easily appreciated.

2. In padahastasana (positions 3 and 10), the legs should remain straight. At first, this may mean that the asana will not be performed correctly, but practise will gradually stretch the tendons and muscles of the back and legs, enabling the correct posture to be assumed.

3. Once both hands are placed on the floor on either side of the feet in position 3 (padahastasana), they should remain at this point until leaving position 10. Similarly, when the feet have been placed together in position 5 (parvatasana), they should remain at this point until moving out of position 8. If the hands and feet are correctly placed initially, there is no need to move them in compensation during the middle series of exercises.

4. When performing ashwa sanchalanasana (positions 4 and 9), the knee of the extended leg should touch the floor. The foot of the other leg should remain between the hands.

5. In parvatasana (positions 5 and 8), try to bring the heels onto the floor. Once again, this may be difficult at first, but practice will stretch the hamstring muscles, bringing the heels closer.

6. Confusion often occurs while moving from position 5 (parvatasana) to position 6 (ashtanga namaskara). The following points may be observed. From position 5, simply bend the knees until they touch the floor. Then bend the elbows, moving the torso straight down, until chest and chin touch the floor also. This will naturally arch the spine and keep the buttocks raised.

Similarly, when moving into position 7 (bhujangasana), the trunk can be pushed forward, straightening the legs, until the body is flat on the floor. Then, with the help of the arms, raise the torso into position. Dividing each asana into stages, and taking each slowly, will give a better coordination and understanding of the correct postures.

7. Retaining the exhaled breath in position 6 (ashtanga namaskara), may prove difficult at the beginning, or if the series is performed slowly. In this case it is advised to either

move from position 5, through 6 into 7 in one continuous movement, pausing only in positions 5 and 7, or to hold position 6 and adjust the breath according to your needs.

8. Older and weaker practitioners may find the effort of pushing up from position 7 (bhujangasana) into position 8 (parvatasana) too great. For them, it is advisable to move from bhujangasana into a position with hands and knees on the floor (as in marjariasana). From this posture, the movement into parvatasana is less difficult.

9. If the full series of 12 postures proves too strenuous, a modified form of 9 postures can be practised. This consists of moving from positions 1 to 5 and back up again from 8 to 12, leaving out the middle group of postures (6 and 7).

Number of rounds

There can be no set rules as to how many rounds of surya namaskara are practised, however, it should never be continued up to the point of exhaustion. The practitioner should become aware of his own physical condition and limitations, and avoid strain at all times. Please remember that surya namaskara is a powerful practice which, if overdone, can lead to unpleasant aches and pains and the symptoms of internal cleansing such as acute inflammation, boils, rashes, colds or even diarrhea. These symptoms quickly subside with rest.

As a suggested program, beginners can start off with 2 to 3 rounds performed slowly, and as the physical condition improves, work up to 12 rounds. A good daily practice is 6 rounds performed slowly then 6 quickly. Advanced students can practise 24 to 54 rounds daily, and in special cases, diseases, or to purify the body, a daily practice of 108 rounds may be undertaken, but only under competent guidance.

After completing the required number of rounds, the practitioner should relax in shavasana for a few minutes.

When and where to practise

The ideal time to practise surya namaskara is at sunrise, the most peaceful time of day, when the atmosphere is full of the sun's ultraviolet rays, so important to the body.

Make a habit of rising early, answering the calls of nature, taking a bath, and practising surya namaskara. Whenever possible, practise in the open air, wearing light and loose clothing to allow the skin to breathe and to absorb the sun's energy.

Surya namaskara is ideally practised facing the sunrise, on a blanket spread over the floor or ground. If it is not possible in the early morning, then the practice can be done at any convenient time, provided the stomach is empty. No food should be taken for at least three to four hours beforehand. In the evening before dinner is also a good time to practise, as it stimulates the digestive fire.

Overcoming bodily stiffness

Sometimes stiffness or structural defects in the body make it impossible to perform each movement fully. In this case the teacher can advise suitable variations until the body becomes supple enough, or the defect is overcome.

Stiffness in the body can be due to three main causes:
1. Muscular tension and muscle bulk,
2. Tightness in the tendons and ligaments,
3. Toxic deposits in the joints.

Regular practice, particularly performing the movements slowly and holding the postures with as much relaxation as possible, will overcome all of these problems. Those who are used to body building exercises need not fear losing strength or reducing muscle bulk through yoga. Surya namaskara leads to flexibility, endurance and efficient use of muscles. Not only do the muscle groups coordinate, but yoga trains us to develop coordination within the structure of the muscle itself leading to greater overall strength.

Holding each posture allows the muscles and tendons time to stretch a little. Once the tendons have been stretched, they will remain that way and maintain a degree of suppleness in the body.

The joints can be kept supple with regular practice, and by a toxin free diet, preferably vegetarian. Reduction of salt intake also helps. For those with extremely stiff bodies, the pawanmuktasana series of exercises is recommended as preparation for surya namaskara.

Limitations

There are no limitations as far as age is concerned. Surya namaskara can be practised beneficially throughout all stages of growth, maturity and old age. However, elderly people are advised to avoid over exertion. As a rule children under 8 years of age, if they can perform surya namaskara, usually do not need it.

Surya namaskara should not be practised by people with high blood pressure, coronary artery disease, or those who have had a stroke, as it may overstimulate or damage a weak heart or blood vessel system. Nor should it be practised in cases of hernia or intestinal tuberculosis.

People with spinal problems should consult a medical expert before commencing surya namaskara. Although many spinal problems can be alleviated through this practice, in some cases, such as slipped disc and sciatica, a program of other yoga asana is more beneficial.

Most women can benefit by practising surya namaskara, even during menstruation. However, those with heavy or painful periods may feel, as a precaution, not to practise at this time. During pregnancy surya namaskara can be practised until the beginning of the 12th week. Following childbirth, it may be gradually commenced for retoning of the uterine muscles, approximately 40 days after delivery.

The most important point to keep in mind, however, is not to strain. Surya namaskara teaches us to tune in with our own capabilities and limitations. With time and practice, you will find these limitations receding. By developing sensitivity to the body, we can use surya namaskara to greatly increase our awareness, health, and wellbeing.

23

Shavasana

Shavasana, the yogic pose of relaxation, should be practised with breath awareness after completing surya namaskara. It rests and relieves any tensions which may be present in the body. Shavasana, known as the dead man's pose, involves consciously willing the entire body to relax to the point where it becomes as limp as a lifeless corpse. Through shavasana complete rest is obtained in a few minutes and afterwards one is able to rise fully refreshed with body and mind in a state of relaxed harmony.

The relaxation period following surya namaskara is an important part of the practice as it allows the body time for readjustment and removal of any toxins which have been released into the bloodstream during the practice. In surya namaskara, some exertion is required to perform the sequence of postures. This is indicated by the increased heart rate and deep breathing, which correspond to arousal of the sympathetic nervous system. The relaxation in shavasana afterwards allows the parasympathetic nervous system to operate, reversing the effects of arousal, and returning the body to a balanced state. Through the combination of surya namaskara and shavasana, both aspects of the autonomic nervous system are stimulated and consequently the whole body is revitalized.

The period of relaxation should last at least until the practitioner can feel that his heartbeat and breath have returned to normal and all tension has been released from the muscles.

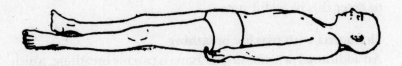

Technique
After completing the practice of surya namaskara, stand erect and take a few deep breaths, then lie down flat on your back in shavasana. Your feet should be slightly apart, arms separate from the body, with the palms facing upward and eyes gently closed. Adjust yourself comfortably, then relax and become perfectly still.

Now bring your awareness down to your feet. Do not move or become tense, simply be aware of them. Try to feel whether your feet are tense, and if you discover any tension, consciously relax them.

When your feet are completely relaxed, slowly draw your awareness up to your ankles and lower legs. Relax these parts in the same way, and continue moving the awareness up to your thighs, hips and buttocks. Pause for a moment and feel that your whole body from the waist downwards is relaxed.

Then gradually proceed upward, one step at a time, to your lower abdomen, navel, upper abdomen, chest, back, hands, lower arms, elbows, upper arms and shoulders. Now pause again to make sure that your whole body from the shoulders down, is totally relaxed. If you discover tension in any part, simply become aware of it for a few moments and the tension will melt away.

Next, move on to the throat, chin, mouth, nose, cheeks, ears, eyes, forehead, top of the head, back of the head, whole head.

Finally become aware of your whole body. Have an all-pervading awareness of the whole body, with no movement or tension in any part. Your body should feel limp and lifeless like a dead corpse. This is the state of total relaxation achieved in shavasana. The whole process from the feet to the head takes only a few minutes. Repeat it a number of times, if necessary, to enter this peaceful state.

Shavasana with psychic breathing

An additional practice in shavasana is psychic breathing, which involves becoming aware of the breathing processes within the different psychic passages of the body. In our body there are many subtle channels through which the prana or vitality flows. We are not ordinarily aware of these movements due to the externalized condition of our minds, but by withdrawing the consciousness and fixing it on the breath, we can develop the ability to perceive and comprehend the workings of these subtle forces which manifest in us as health, activity (mental as well as physical), and life itself, especially after surya namaskara.

While lying down in shavasana with the whole body totally relaxed and still, become aware of the natural flow of the breath. Do not alter your breathing in any way, simply transfer your awareness from the body to the breath. Feel every breath with complete and total attention – the expansion and relaxation of the lungs, the rise and fall of the abdomen. Don't miss a single breath, and soon you will find that your whole mind has become relaxed and absorbed in the breathing process.

Now you are ready to begin psychic breathing awareness. Bring your mind to the navel and as you inhale, imagine that the breath is moving upward through a special passage to the throat. On exhalation, the breath descends back down the passage to the navel. You have to imagine there is a small passageway between the navel and throat through which the air is moving.

Now begin counting every breath from navel to throat, throat to navel. Start from 50 and count backwards to 0, each complete respiration is one round. If you lose track go back and start again.

26

Alternate nostril breathing

Now leave your awareness of the psychic passage between the navel and the throat and become aware of the breath in the nose, excluding everything else. As you inhale, concentrate on the left nostril and feel the air entering from the left side only. As you exhale, concentrate on the right nostril, and feel the breath being expelled from the right side only. On the next inhalation maintain awareness of the right nostril, then with exhalation change to the left nostril. Now again, left in, right out, right in, left out; left in, right out, right in, left out. Begin counting – left in, right out, 50; right in, left out, 49; and so on backwards to 0. When you have completed this, stop breath awareness and bring your awareness back to the body. Then mentally chant Om three times. Sit up and open your eyes.

Psychic Centers

In the subtle body of man there are seven major psychic centers called chakras. They have their physical representation in the various nerve plexuses and endocrine glands. During surya namaskara these points are used for focusing the mind, and developing concentration and awareness. Concentration in these areas allows us to activate the chakras and to tap into the higher psychic and spiritual energy which is associated with their increased functioning. The related physical structures also benefit greatly through this enhanced awareness.

The actual compression of the physical correlates of each psychic center by any asana has a stimulating effect on the chakra involved. This is mediated through the compression, stimulation and rebalancing of the nervous and endocrine components. However, the activation of psychic centers through surya namaskara proceeds mainly through the development of internal awareness, concentration and visualization. The actual physical stimulation from each asana enhances prana shakti, allowing us to better focus and concentrate our mental and physical energies at the chakra location. It is this dual aspect of taking our mental awareness to a highly charged physical structure which leads to fusion of mind and body, ida and pingala, and which ignites the chakra. This initiation culminates in spiritual awareness.

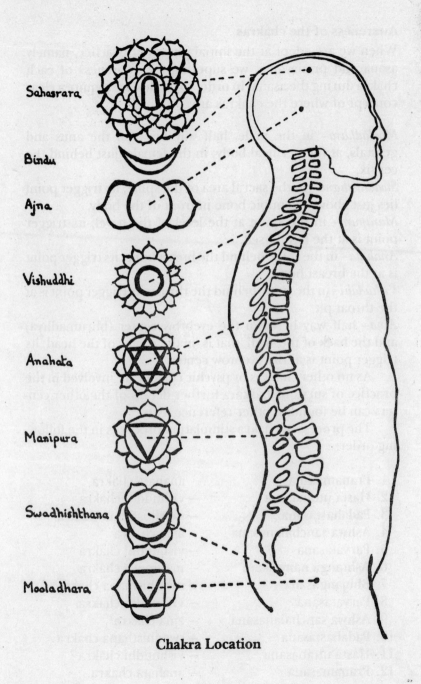

Sahasrara

Bindu

Ajna

Vishuddhi

Anahata

Manipura

Swadhishthana

Mooladhara

Chakra Location

29

Awareness of the chakras

When we are adept at the initial phases of practice, namely asana and pranayama, we superimpose awareness of each chakra during the asana. In order to do this, we require a clear concept of where the chakras are:

Mooladhara– in the male, half way between the anus and genitals, at the perineal body; in the female, just behind the cervix.

Swadhisthana– in the sacral area of the spine; its trigger point lies just above the pubic bone in front of the body.

Manipura– in the spine at the level of the navel; its trigger point is at the navel itself.

Anahata– in the spine behind the breast bone; its trigger point is at the breast bone.

Vishuddhi– in the spine behind the throat; its trigger point is at the throat pit.

Ajna– half way between the eyebrow center (bhrumadhya) and the back of the skull, that is, in the center of the head; its trigger point is at the eyebrow center.

As no other chakras or psychic centers are involved in the practice of surya namaskara further details of the other centers can be found in other reference texts.

The process of chakra stimulation proceeds in the following order:

1. Pranamasana	— anahata chakra
2. Hasta uttanasana	— vishuddhi chakra
3. Padahastasana	— swadhisthana chakra
4. Ashwa sanchalanasana	— ajna chakra
5. Parvatasana	— vishuddhi chakra
6. Ashtanga namaskara	— manipura chakra
7. Bhujangasana	— swadhisthana chakra
8. Parvatasana	— vishuddhi chakra
9. Ashwa sanchalanasana	— ajna chakra
10. Padahastasana	— swadhisthana chakra
11. Hasta uttanasana	— vishuddhi chakra
12. Pranamasana	— anahata chakra

Piercing the chakras

While practising each asana we endeavor to locate the chakra associated with it and develop our concentration of that center. For this, some time is required, especially in the initial stages. However, no more than one minute should be spent on each asana unless you are practising under guidance. As we increase the proficiency with which we locate the chakras we can speed up the practice.

As proficiency in chakra awareness and visualization improves, the process of asana, pranayama and chakra awareness can be fused. One can utilize the breath to increase stimulation of the chakras. For example, visualize the psychic breath carrying prana into the body via the chakra as you inhale and flowing out of the body as you exhale. During breath retention become aware of the meeting of prana and apana in manipura. Of course, these types of advanced practices should be learned under expert guidance for at this level surya namaskara becomes a part of the preparatory practices for kundalini yoga.

In the practice of surya namaskara we mentally touch all the chakras of the body, except for mooladhara chakra. This develops the other chakras in preparation for the awakening of kundalini from mooladhara. The body must be strong and healthy in order to withstand the power of mooladhara awakening which is associated with the release of powerful, unconscious forces. Surya namaskara increases vitality in preparation for this event. Then other practices can be used to awaken mooladhara when the time is right.

One may combine chakra concentration with mental repetition of the mantras, by feeling that the mantra is being repeated in or on the chakra. When the practitioner's concentration develops to a higher degree he may even feel that the vibrations of the mantras are issuing forth from the psychic centers, a most wonderful and intense experience.

Sun Mantras

All the external sounds which we perceive are created when two or more objects, such as the vocal cords, strike together and set up a vibration in the atmosphere. These vibrations then enter the ear, in turn setting up vibrations in the eardrum and its fluid. The nature of these vibrations is relayed to the brain where they are acknowledged and compared to the memory of all past sounds, and mental images are then created. In this way sound is continuously affecting our minds.

Mantras are combinations of sounds, which are designed to produce a specific effect on the mind and its functioning. The mantra can be spoken aloud, whispered or repeated mentally, but mental repetition is the superior method. When a sound is mentally repeated with awareness and concentration, the thought takes on the form of that sound, it becomes that sound, and the energy inherent in that sound manifests in the mind.

Mantras are formulated from letters of the Sanskrit alphabet, each letter having its own particular vibrational frequency and corresponding effect on the consciousness. These fifty two sounds, known as *Devanagari*, were realized by the ancient rishis of the vedic period during deep states of meditation. These highly evolved souls were able to touch on the source of all sound energy, the shabda brahman, the supreme consciousness manifesting as sound.

The twelve sun mantras

Every year the sun passes through twelve different phases: known as the zodiacal signs in western astrology, and as the *rashis* in Hindu astrology. According to Hindu astrology, each rashi has specific attributes or moods, and in each of these twelve moods the sun is given a different name. These twelve names comprise the twelve sun mantras, which are to be mentally repeated in their respective order in conjunction with the twelve movements of surya namaskara.

These sun mantras are not merely names of the sun, but every sound syllable contained in them is the vehicle of a basic, eternal energy (shakti) represented by the sun itself. By repetition and concentration on these mantras, the whole mental structure will benefit and be uplifted.

Although these mantras do not require intellectual understanding, a translation of their meaning is given below for those with an enquiring mind as well as for the more spiritually inclined who wish to use the mantras as a form of attunement with the source of spiritual illumination symbolized by the sun.

1. *Om Mitraya Namaha*
(Salutations to the friend of all)

The first position, pranamasana, embodies the attitude of reverence to the source of all life as we know it: the sun is regarded as the universal friend, endlessly giving light, heat and energy to support this and all the other planets. In the scriptures, Mitra is described as calling men to activity, sustaining earth and sky, and beholding all creatures without discrimination, just as the early morning sun signals the beginning of the day's activities, and sheds its light on all life.

2. *Om Ravaye Namaha*
(Salutations to the shining one)

Ravaye means one who shines and offers divine blessings upon all life. In the second position, hasta uttanasana, we are stretching our whole being upwards, towards the source of light, to receive these blessings.

3. *Om Sūryāya Namaha*
(Salutations to he who induces activity)

Here the sun is in a very dynamic aspect as the deity, Surya. In ancient vedic mythology Surya was worshipped as the Lord of the Heavens, pictured crossing the sky in his fiery chariot, drawn by seven horses. This is a beautiful analogy and needs a correct interpretation. The seven horses actually represent the seven rays or emanations of the supreme consciousness, which manifest as the seven planes of existence, bhu (earthly, material), bhuvar (intermediate, astral), suwar (subtle, heavenly), mahar (the abode of the devas), janah (the abode of divine souls who have transcended ego), tapah (the abode of enlightened siddhas) and satyam (the ultimate truth of reality). Surya symbolizes the supreme consciousness itself, in control of all these different planes of manifestation. Surya is regarded as the most concrete of the solar gods, one of the original vedic triad, his place being in the sky, while Agni (fire) is his representative on earth.

4. *Om Bhānave Namaha*
(Salutations to he who illumines)

The sun is the physical representation of the guru or teacher, who removes the darkness of our delusions, just as the darkness of the night is removed with every dawn. In the fourth position, ashwa sanchalanasana, we turn our face towards this illumination and pray for an end to the dark night of ignorance.

5. *Om Khagāya Namaha*
(Salutations to the one who moves through the sky)

It is the sun's daily movement through the sky which is the basis of our measurement of time, from the earliest use of a sun dial to the sophisticated devices used today. In parvatasana, we offer obeisances to the one by whom time is measured, and pray for progress in life.

6. *Om Pushne Namaha*
(Salutations to the giver of strength and nourishment)

The sun is the source of all strength. Like a father, he nourishes us with energy, light and life. We offer respects in ashtanga namaskara by touching all the eight corners of our body to the ground. In essence we are offering our whole being in the hope that he may bestow mental, physical and spiritual strength and nourishment upon us.

7. *Om Hiranya Garbhāya Namaha*
(Salutations to the golden cosmic self)

Hiranya Garbha is also known as the golden egg, resplendent as the sun, in which Brahma was born as the manifestation of Self-existence. Hiranya Garbha is the seed of causality, thus the whole universe is contained within Hiranya Garbha in the potential state prior to manifestation. In the same way, all life is potential in the sun, which represents the great cosmic principle. We offer respects to the sun in bhujangasana, the seventh position, praying for the awakening of creativity.

8. *Om Marichaye Namaha*
(Salutations to the rays of the sun)

Maricha is one of Brahma's sons, just as the rays of light are produced from the sun, but his name also means mirage. For our whole life, we seek after a true meaning or purpose, like the thirsty man seeks after water in a desert, but is fooled by mirages dancing on the horizon produced by the sun's rays.

In the eighth position, parvatasana, we pray for true illumination and discrimination in order to be able to distinguish between the real and the unreal.

9. *Om Ādityāya Namaha*
(Salutations to the son of Aditi)

Aditi is one of the many names given to the cosmic mother, Mahashakti. She is the mother of all the gods, boundless and inexhaustible, the creative power from which all divisions of power proceed. The sun is one of her children, or manifestations. In the ninth position, ashwa sanchalanasana, we salute Aditi, the infinite cosmic mother.

35

10. *Om Savitre Namaha*
(Salutations to the stimulating power of the sun)

Savitre is known as the stimulator, the arouser, and is often associated with Surya who also represents the same posture, padahastasana. Savitre is said to represent the sun before rising, stimulating and arousing man into waking activity, and Surya is said to represent the sun after sunrise, when activity begins. Therefore, in the tenth position, padahastasana, we salute Savitre to obtain the vivifying power of the sun.

11. *Om Arkaya Namaha*
(Salutations to he who is fit to be praised)

Arka means 'energy'. The sun is the source of most of the energy in the world we know. In the eleventh position, hasta uttanasana, we are offering respects to this source of life and energy.

12. *Om Bhaskaraya Namaha*
(Salutations to the one who leads to enlightenment)

In this final salutation we offer respects to the sun as a symbol of the great revealer of all transcendental and spiritual truths. He lights up the pathway leading to our ultimate goal of liberation. In the twelfth position, pranamasana, we pray that this pathway may be revealed to us.

Bija mantras

As an alternative to the twelve names of the sun, there is a series of bija mantras, or seed syllables. The bija mantras are evocative sounds that have no literal meaning in themselves, but set up very powerful vibrations of energy within the mind and body.

The bija mantras are:

1. *Om Hram*   ॐ ह्राम्
2. *Om Hrim*   ॐ ह्रीम्
3. *Om Hroom*   ॐ ह्रूम्
4. *Om Hraim*   ॐ ह्रैम्
5. *Om Hraum*   ॐ ह्रौम्
6. *Om Hraha*   ॐ ह:

36

The six bija mantras are repeated four times during one complete round of surya namaskara.

Either the bija mantras or the sun mantras can be recited aloud or mentally depending mainly on inclination of the practitioner and the speed of practice. If the speed is very slow then the sun mantras can be combined with chakra awareness. If the speed is a little faster, then the bija mantras can be utilized in the same way. If the physical movements are done a little more quickly, then either the mantras can be recited alone without chakra rotation, or awareness can be rotated through the chakras without mantra.

Surya Namaskara for Children

Children are complete but unexpressed personalities. They are the seed within which the whole is contained, but in potential form. We see the mysterious transformations of life all around and within us everyday, yet we still do not understand the process. How can we really help our children grow if we ourselves are not masters of our own life forces. Only a master gardener knows how much water, fertilizer and pruning a plant needs. In the same way, if we are not masters, then we should not try to prune our children, lest we cut off some essential part that may never grow back.

Guru is the master gardener of the body, mind and soul. He knows how to guide the child's growth through all stages of development. As a simple formula, the spiritual masters of old prescribed surya namaskara along with simple nadi shodhana pranayama and gayatri mantra for children from the age of 8 years. Thus the integral development of children was assured from an early age.

Surya namaskara in the classroom

Today our children sit in overcrowded classrooms, cramped and bent over their books, their minds tired from too much intellectual activity. Education is taken to mean that we enter an institution in order to gain the intellectual skills and capacity for a job or profession. However, real education is not just for the fulfillment of external, social and economic commitments, but it is also for our inner understanding and the growth of our personality at all levels, physical, mental and spiritual.

Recently there has been a call by educators for increased depth and breadth to the education system. These people want the intuitive and creative side of a child's personality and mind developed, in order to redress the existing imbalances which may be the cause of many of our present problems in life.

Surya namaskara, nadi shodhana pranayama and gayatri mantra can be utilized to tap this potential and to develop not only the intellect but also the intuition. Thus balance is achieved.

Swami Yogabhakti Saraswati (Mlle M. Flack), founder of Satyanandashram Paris and a teacher in the C.E.S. Condorcet High School, has made extensive study of the use of surya namaskara in the classroom to bring the intellectual and intuitive sides of children into balance. She states:

"In the opinion of parents, children and teachers alike, teaching yoga practices such as surya namaskara to children has been a success in our school. Many parents have suggested that these practices which have already been seen to have a stabilizing effect on their children, should be continued at school. The only question raised here was that of training more teachers in these methods."

Already, teachers and principals throughout the world have taken up this work and begun to introduce surya namaskara and other relevant yoga practices into the school systems. Everywhere they are finding that a few minutes practise before the class, makes the children more eager to learn, attentive, receptive, responsive and communicative. Surya namaskara is an excellent method to constructively utilize the exuberant physical energy that most children possess, so as to channel it towards physical and mental health. After this series of asanas the children are better prepared to take in the subject matter in the next lesson.

Balancing the emotion

The importance of balancing a child's emotions in terms of their future life can be readily appreciated. We should keep this in mind when we examine the function of surya namaskara in establishing and enhancing their mental and emotional stability.

At the age of eight years the pineal gland starts to calcify and decay so that by the age of twelve to fourteen years puberty begins. The pineal holds the pituitary hormones, responsible for sexual maturity, in check and prevents precocious puberty. Its premature decay often allows over rapid sexual development. The physical aspect, the development of new sensations and desires, outstrips the mental, producing imbalance. A young mind is unable to understand and deal with the rapid development of the new feelings in a mature way, resulting in emotional trauma and the 'identity crisis' so prevalent in the early teens. It can also lead to severe hormonal imbalance and a variety of diseases, both physical and mental.

What we seek to achieve in yogic practice, is maintenance of the pineal gland, thereby delaying sexual development for a few years. When emotional development catches up to the physical component, the physical ripening can proceed in a controlled manner, free from the emotional traumas which leave permanent scars later on.

Surya namaskara combined with nadi shodhana pranayama, shambavi mudra and gayatri mantra is the ancient method prescribed by the yogis and rishis to slow down pineal degeneration. These practices help to maintain the whole ajna chakra complex which is seated at the pineal. If this can be achieved, life will be smoother sailing. When children are not able to balance the mental and physical aspects of their being, what happens? If there is excessive mental energy, the child becomes a daydreamer, but is unable to express himself. On the other hand, excess physical energy makes him a terror, impossible to manage. Therefore, balance of these two poles of our existence is essential, if we are to help our children grow into healthy and mature adults.

40

Developing a new race of man

Surya namaskara is a practice that allows the shaping of the human personality to take place from the early age of eight years. A child who is lucky enough to receive this type of training will have many advantages over his fellow students who have received the purely intellectual education prevalent today.

The yogic education fulfills the criterion laid down by the great physiologist and humanist Alexis Carrel:

"The development of young human beings between the sixth and eighteenth years of life should take place simultaneously in the anatomical, functional, organic, skeletal, muscular, physiological, intellectual and emotional aspects. In none of these spheres can development occur separately. The most important of these spheres are the physiological and emotional aspects and education should begin from there. In the first place a psycho-physiological discipline should be introduced, and at the same time the principles governing interhuman relationships should be inculcated."

The above statement points to the necessity of introducing basic yogic training, which includes the practice of surya namaskara, to our youth in order to produce a controlled and integrated unfoldment of psychic and physical functions which would develop a new race of man. Quoting the words of the great humanist and physician, Albert Schweitzer:

"There must come a new renaissance reaching much deeper than the one which led us out of the middle ages, a great renaissance when humanity will find that ethical values are the highest truth and the most useful value. This will liberate the human race from the senseless reality in which it is now vegetating."

Pranic Generator

Surya namaskara is a technique of solar vitalization, a series of exercises which charges us like a battery, enabling us to live more fully and joyfully with dynamism and skill in action. It seems that the practice was devised with two main aims in mind: first, to maintain good physical health as part of an enlightened system of living, and second, to prepare for techniques of kundalini yoga and spiritual awakening.

The benefits gained through regular practice of surya namaskara far surpass ordinary physical exercise and at the same time enhance sports and other forms of physical recreation. This is due to its direct vitalizing effect on the solar energies of the body, centered at manipura chakra and flowing in pingala nadi. At the same time, when the asanas are performed with pranayama or in concert with yogic sadhana, they lead to a balanced system of energies at both the physical and mental levels. To fully understand this, we require basic knowledge about the psychic framework of nadis which motivates the physical body.

The dual aspect of life

We live in a world of duality: day/night, light/dark, good/bad, introversion/extroversion, knowledge/action, and so on. We inhabit a world of polarities, which has been symbolically represented in yoga as ida and pingala, and in many other philosophies, for example, the yin and yang of taoism. These symbols can be used to help us understand our universe at all levels.

According to the yoga shastras, it is the underlying energy structure which gives our body life. Scriptural texts cite 72,000 nadis or flows of energy throughout the human body. These flows have various interpenetrating and interdependent levels, just as a sound has harmonics and subharmonics. They may be physical (nervous, circulatory, lymphatic, etc.), pranic (more subtle currents of energy still relating to the physical body such as metabolism), mental (thought currents) or psychic (dreams or visions). Pingala nadi conducts prana shakti (vital energy) and ida nadi conducts manas shakti (mental energy). The following table indicates the characteristics of these twin energy flows:

Ida	Pingala
Breath flows through left nostril	Breath flows through right nostril
Introversion	Extroversion
Awareness	Energy and action
Mind	Prana
Negative	Positive
Coolness	Heat
Female	Male
Inactive	Active
Moon	Sun
Subjectivity	Objectivity
Intuition	Analytic logic
Left side of the body	Right side of the body
Right side of the brain	Left side of the brain

The number of possible attributes for ida and pingala are endless, for we see this dual property in all of nature. Both the macrocosm and the microcosm, which is the body of man, are based on these two polarities, for example, arteries/veins, sympathetic/parasympathetic nerves, sodium/potassium in the conduction of nerve impulses, and so on.

Awakening the spiritual force

When the dual aspects of ida and pingala merge, a third force comes into existence. This force is the flow of spiritual energy in sushumna nadi. Its awakening can only occur when ida and pingala are perfectly balanced. In man, this awakening of sushumna correlates with the awakening of energy in the spinal cord. The energy liberated transports the individual awareness to the transcendental spiritual realms beyond time and space. Before this awakening can occur, however, the mind and body must be adequately prepared over a long period of time, and the energies must be flowing sufficiently and evenly.

Surya namaskara forms a basic part of the ongoing release of pranic energy and the balancing of pingala nadi. A healthy body and an active waking life are the basis for spiritual development. Too many philosophies in the past have disregarded this most basic point. Unless the physical component can be balanced and integrated into the total structure of man, awakening of the inner light cannot occur. Evolution, especially on the spiritual level, requires balance, otherwise darkness and ignorance continue to prevail.

Physiopranic effects

In order to understand how surya namaskara works on the pranic body and nadis, we need to have both practical experience and a clear understanding of how each asana works individually. Then we can understand the practice as a whole. We must also remember that we are not just dealing with asanas but also with pranayama, chakra awareness and mantra, which magnify the effects one thousandfold.

1. **Pranamasana** (prayer pose) induces a state of introversion, relaxation, and calmness, and obviously activates the anahata chakra.

2. **Hasta uttanasana** (raised arms pose) stretches the body upward and backward. The muscles of the back and neck are relaxed and the front of the chest and abdomen are stretched. This, combined with deep inhalation, gives a gentle massage to the abdominal contents, improving digestion. The upward

stretch gives traction to the spine, helping to maintain health of the spongy discs between the vertebrae and toning the spinal nerves. The arms and shoulders are relaxed and roundness removed. This pose is also said to remove excess weight, which may occur because of its effect on vishuddhi chakra and the thyroid gland, speeding up the metabolism. Prana is lifted upwards to the upper parts of the body, propelled by inhalation.

3. **Padahastasana** (hands to feet pose) combines the effects of an inverted pose, with those of a forward bending pose. It massages the abdominal contents, especially the liver, kidneys, gall bladder, pancreas, adrenal glands, uterus and ovaries. The whole abdomen is toned, eliminating many ailments, such as constipation. The power of digestion increases and female disorders such as prolapse and menstrual irregularities are relieved. A good flow of blood is encouraged to the spinal nerves as they are stretched and toned. The hamstring and calf muscles are also stretched, relieving varicose veins and aiding the return of blood to the heart. Inversion increases blood flow to the brain. The combination of inversion and forward bending is a powerful means of toning the whole body, as pressure is exerted on all the major endocrine glands–genitals, adrenals, thymus, thyroid and parathyroids, pineal and pituitary. Major emphasis is given to the pelvic stretch and swadhisthana chakra. Prana is channelled to the lower regions of the body, motivated by exhalation. When prana moves downward it is called apana.

4. **Ashwa sanchalanasana** (equestrian pose), gives a backward bend to the spine so as to relax the back muscles. The abdominal area is also stretched as a consequence. The main stretch, however, is in the pelvic region. The pelvis is pushed down and forward as one leg is placed forward while the other is stretched as far back as possible. Concentration is placed at the eyebrow center, ajna chakra, which is directly linked with mooladhara. The energies liberated in the pelvic region thereby, help to stimulate ajna. Prana moves upward with inhalation along a nadi which can be felt along the front of the thigh, running upward along the front side of the body right

45

up to the ajna chakra region. If your sinuses are blocked while performing this asana you will feel an immediate sense of relief as each side is stretched.

5. **Parvatasana** (mountain pose), also called *sumeru asana* (summit pose), physically strengthens the nerves and muscles in the arms and legs, stretches the calf muscles and achilles tendons, and makes the spine straight and taut. It is an asana which relieves varicose veins as well as toning the spinal nerves. It is said to stimulate vishuddhi chakra, because the chin is placed on the chest, compressing the thyroid gland. Prana moves downward with exhalation.

6. **Ashtanga namaskara** (salutation with eight limbs), develops the chest and strengthens the arms, shoulders and legs. It accentuates the normal spinal curves and sends additional blood to this area helping to rejuvenate the nerves. The back muscles experience profound relaxation in this posture which is said to stimulate manipura chakra. One can feel the increased release of energy from this center as the spinal cord is squeezed from top to bottom in this position. As the breath is held in external retention, bahir kumbhaka, the prana moves down to manipura where the meeting of prana and apana takes place in the adept.

7. **Bhujangasana** (cobra pose), gives dynamic compression to the contents of the chest and abdomen, relieving many ailments, such as asthma, constipation, indigestion, kidney and liver problems, and so on. As a means of releasing tension in the back muscles and spinal nerves, it is one of the best asanas because it stretches each vertebrae from top to bottom sequentially as the position is assumed. This pose pulls the spinal column forward towards the head, and this exerts a subtle traction on the lower end of the spine at swadhisthana chakra.

Because of inhalation, prana tends to move upwards in this posture, however, we place our awareness at the swadhisthana area in an attempt to stimulate prana at the source of the upward flow. Prana also tends to move upwards spontaneously because it has been held down during the previous two postures.

46

The combined effect

The physical body is composed of matter and energy. The actual physical movements forward and backward are enough to enhance our metabolic rate and release energy. When combined with chakra stimulation, the effects are enhanced.

The spinal cord, the link between the brain and the body, is the conduit for all our energies. Within it are the ida and pingala nadis, so its health is of paramount importance. Surya namaskara, being an active and dynamic series exerts its major influence on pingala nadi, especially when it is practised quickly. However, when practised slowly and completely with chakras and mantras it stimulates both ida and pingala almost equally, depending on the practitioner's abilities.

When we practise surya namaskara slowly, less emphasis is given to pingala nadi and more time is given to mental development. The practice transforms itself from a series of asanas to a series of mudras leading to a more balanced development. It is for this reason that we recommend a combination of both fast and slow practice, for most of us require a little extra pingala stimulation and refinement because of the nature of our present day lifestyles. Before we can delve into the human psyche with mudras or meditation, we must first make our bodies strong and healthy. The channels for the elimination of impurities must be free. Basically, we can all do with a little more physical exercise.

The pranic channels of the body are cleansed by the enhancement and control of the movement of prana in the body. As each asana aids and accentuates the natural flow of prana up and down, blockages are removed. After the series is completed these flows move with greater ease and improve body functions. This is the constructive channelling of energy rather than allowing it to dissipate.

Constructive channelling, or rather rechannelling due to the unblocking effect, is enhanced by manipura chakra stimulation. Though we do not consciously concentrate on manipura more than twice in any one round, it is profoundly affected by the practice and at the same time lends power to the flows of energy in pingala nadi.

Manipura chakra is situated at the navel, the approximate center of gravity of the body. Manipura means 'jewelled city'. It is linked to the solar plexus, which is a bundle of nerves fanning out from a central plexus, like the rays of the sun. The solar plexus is governed by the sympathetic nervous system, pingala nadi, and is responsible for the digestion and assimilation of nutrients. At a macrocosmic level the sun is also responsible for the growth of plants and manufacture of food. It is, therefore, very important in terms of our physical health. Surya namaskara flexes and extends the body, stretching and compressing the center of gravity and giving it maximum stimulation. Apart from being good for digestion, the whole body is charged with vitality when manipura chakra is healthy.

Once we have undergone the preliminary training with surya namaskara and become acquainted with it, we have to move in a stepwise, systematic approach. First we slowly stretch the physical structures, muscles and tendons and stimulate the inner organs. Once we become aware of our physical limitations and start to overcome them, we can proceed on to pranic awareness and work through the various obstacles and blockages at this level. Eventually we learn to control our prana, to manipulate and adjust it as we desire. Then we are ready for the next state which is the extension of prana in the subtle psychic and mental levels.

48

Psychodynamics

In yogic physiology the body consists of physical, pranic, mental, intuitive and spiritual components. The more subtle aspects are the more powerful. Mind drives the body. For example, if we can induce a state of mind in which we visualize positive, vitalizing images we can alter a negative state such as depression, anxiety or lethargy. This is because the mind and body are inseparable. They are intimate and in the final analysis depend on each other for their existence. At the same time the power of the mind is unimaginable.

Yogic techniques aim at developing flexibility in the body and mind. Through meditative practices such as antar mouna, we ultimately reach a point where we throw out any unwanted thoughts or feelings before they can affect our equilibrium. To reach this stage requires practice, experience and guidance. Until such an event takes place in the life of a man or woman, until we have a conscious choice over the contents of our mind, we need other techniques to help induce a positive, creative state.

Surya namaskara, as already mentioned, has an effect on ida as well as pingala nadi. This is especially true when we perform the practice slowly and even more enhanced with the use of mantras or chakras. At the same time there is another aspect of surya namaskara which helps to induce a positive and vitalized state of mind.

49

Each asana conveys an image to the archetypal depths of our mind. For example, the image of a cobra has a very powerful and dynamic, pingala-type effect. There can be few more powerful and hypnotically awesome creatures in our world. The images conveyed by the mountain pose, the equestrian pose, and the raised arm pose are also very dynamic. It is a beautiful and aesthetic quality of surya namaskara that it encapsulates such dynamic images within the peaceful and sacrosanct prayer pose.

As an exercise in contemplation, visualize each asana of surya namaskara and feel for yourself what the effects of each image are. The following interpretation of the psychodynamic effects of surya namaskara is designed to give depth to the practice and to stimulate each individual to formulate his own interpretation and to look into the depths of his own mind for the intuitive experience of the practice.

Psychodynamic interpretation

Pranamasana, as the first and last pose of the series, marks the beginning and end of the transit of the sun's passage from dawn to dusk. As such, it represents the peace, tranquility and beauty of the sunrise and sunset. It is the calm of the two spiritual times of the day when the forces of dark and light, ida and pingala, merge and produce the third force of sushumna, the spiritual light. It allows us to find our inner equipoise and balance at the start of our busy and energetic day, represented by the more dynamic and strenuous asanas, and also to be able to quickly re-establish serenity when the need for activity is over. Thus, it creates the situation for mental flexibility, from the time when we can be at peace with ourselves in order to gather our resources before diving into the world, until the time when we emerge, having used up our energy in daily activity. As the asana is performed with exhalation this indicates at once introversion, and giving of oneself to the world.

From pranamasana we move to hasta uttanasana in which our hands and head stretch up to their highest point. From this point on, the head and body will gradually move downward so that at the middle of the series the body is at its lowest position while the sun is at its highest. Hasta uttanasana can be seen then, to indicate man drawing in the energy of the newly risen sun, not only via the breath, but through every pore in the body. This is the energy man will use to dive into his busy daily life as represented by the next asana, padahastasana.

Asanas such as padahastasana and parvatasana seem to represent introversion, yet they are rather more symbolic of the introspection necessary to carry out our daily duties, than the deep sense withdrawal of pratyahara. They provide a balance to the extroversion so characteristic of daily life. Padahastasana precedes ashwa sanchalanasana, giving us the feeling of looking inside for the inspiration and answers to the problems which have to be faced squarely and bravely in our daily life. After man has looked to the heavens for inspiration he looks to the earth for balance and stability.

Ashwa sanchalanasana represents the power and courage required to face the problems of life and the self-confidence which arises when we have looked within and made contact with the inner guide (ajna).

Ashtanga namaskara represents the energies of man at their lowest ebb. When the sun is at its extremity, either at noon or at midnight, man is at his most vulnerable period, for this is the time of inertia, or tamas, when most people feel the need for rest or sleep. As such, this asana represents man's complete surrender before the power of the midday sun.

Bhujangasana represents the awakening of man from his sleep, the arising of knowledge from ignorance, the awakening of rajasic vital energy out of the inertia of tamas. When the serpent, representing wisdom arises, man begins his ascent back towards the spiritual, balanced sattwic state.

We see that synchronized with the journey of the physical sun through the various degrees of the heavens, the asanas can represent the state of man's vital energies, of the pingala nadi, from their peak at dawn, to their lowest point at midday (or midnight) and again to a peak at dusk.

Though the above interpretation is only one of many possibilities, the use of such images lends power and depth to

51

the practice and lifts it out of the purely physical. It is images such as these, and their contemplation, which shifts the balance of mental awareness away from the negative and towards the positive. When these are combined with the physical wellbeing experienced due to pingala nadi stimulation, the mental effects are reinforced.

✓   We, therefore, use surya namaskara as a matrix upon which to turn and transform the mind, especially when we hold such images within the mind while practising. Concomitantly, physical vitality and health are enhanced.

The Rhythms of Life

The organs of a healthy body are like the well-tuned instruments of an orchestra which are conducted by the brain and nervous system. Each organ functions in rhythm and harmony with all the other organs of the body, performing at that time of the day when their activity is required. However, an unhealthy body is out of tune and discordant. This occurs when our energy systems are depleted of or oversupplied with vital energy or when one part of the controlling neural circuits is not directing the body appropriately.

The body's daily or diurnal rhythms are set by the environment and by our lifestyle. The inner rhythms must not only be attuned to inner needs but must work in concerted harmony with outer demands and forces. Many of the inner rhythms are set by the daily pattern of light and dark and by our pattern of activity within the daily revolution of the earth as it spins upon its own axis while moving around the sun. Professor Wieslaw Romanowski of the Department of Physiology, Academy of Physical Education, Warsaw, a pioneer worker in the research of yogic asanas, states that:

"Movement and rhythm are characteristic of the universe in which we live... In living organisms certain rhythmic functional changes occur dependent on the periodicity of processes occurring in the outer environment and known as exogenous (external) rhythms. There also exists a specific rhythmicity in the biological unit– endogenous (internal) rhythmicity." (*1)

According to the theory of biorhythms, these internal and external rhythms can be classified according to frequency in the following ways:

1. *Low frequency*, such as seasons and monthly cycles,
2. *Moderate frequency*, such as respiratory and heart cycles,
3. *High frequency*, such as the pulsation of enzymatic systems or the atoms in a crystal.

In our study of surya namaskara, it is the group of moderate frequency rhythms that interests us most, because they are visible and perceptible, and can thus be easily observed by us at any moment. They are the first step to our understanding of the higher and lower frequencies around us. The middle frequency also includes circadian (day/night), cardiac (heart) and peristaltic (abdominal) rhythms.

Modern life has removed man from nature's benign and rhythmic influence. The internal rhythms, the inherent clockwork-like nature of the nervous and endocrine systems, have become imbalanced through the effects of stress and tension, resulting in feelings of discomfort and lack of wellbeing, and leading to disease and neurosis. The brainwaves of most 'normal' people clearly indicate lack of integration between parts of the brain, forming random and asymmetric patterns. In the clinical situation we see this, for example, as one part of the body relaxing while another part is preparing the body for stress. This shows lack of concerted harmony between parts. Rather, organs assume autonomy and act as separate entities (this may be the microcosmic reflection of a macrocosmic situation). The subjective experience is that of disordered thought patterns, mild manic depressive states, inability to concentrate and emotional and mental instability. Or the effects may be severe.

In order to resume normal internal rhythmic function, we have to find some way to adjust the patterns which have become disordered over perhaps many years. This requires tools or techniques that can penetrate into the 'stroma' of the nervous system, its basic meshwork consisting of sensory, motor and autonomic components. It is this stroma which determines such parameters as brainwave patterns, personality, how we think, feel and respond to the world. It is responsible for maintaining habits and conditioned responses, whether sick or healthy. The stroma can be changed if we know how to do it.

Probably the best way to counteract unhealthy body rhythms is to superimpose new psychophysical rhythms of a health promoting nature. Chemicals, shock therapies, new modes of behavior and conditioning, psychological techniques, and many other methods have been utilized over the centuries in an attempt to improve inner function and experience, however, with little success. They do not actually change the neural stroma or radically alter the mental structure and, as a rule, fail to bring lasting changes.

The yogic methods of altering inner rhythms proceed in a slow and systematic way. It does not attempt to radically change anything. Rather it seeks to slowly mold and modify the existing structures by becoming a new and healthgiving extension of our day to day life. It imposes a regular and consistent benevolent force which aims at flowing with and reinforcing the natural inherent body rhythms. It works with nature, not against it. This is why the practices of yoga have to be performed regularly, daily, even if for only a few minutes.

When we perform surya namaskara on a daily basis we add a new factor to our lives; an ordered, sequential, systematic, energizing, cleansing series of postures, breathing, mantras and chakra stimulation. It is like a drug or health tonic taken every day before breakfast. It is as though we were injecting a few particles of prana into the already existing structures. Body growth continues. Metabolism, nerve conduction, endocrinal hormone secretions, daily activities, all go on in their normal natural way, however, a new factor has been added that over the months and years, subtly alters the patterns and rhythms. It is like adding a pinch of salt to food and perceptibly altering the taste.

Imposing a healthy external rhythm onto an already exist-

55

ing rhythm changes it. Imposing a healthy, natural, ordered, harmonizing rhythm such as surya namaskara onto a disordered and diseased rhythm has an even more dramatic effect. Polish researchers, T. Pasek and W. Romanowski state that psycho-prophylactic procedures of which the asanas in surya namaskara form a part, "aim at producing an ordered and stabilized sequence of functional states and relaxation characterized by a biological rhythm". They call this rhythm 'controlled rhythm' to contrast it with the other two natural forms, inner and outer. This mechanism can manipulate the internal rhythms in the same way that a selector on a radio alters the frequency being received.

Surya namaskara emerges as a powerful means to exert conscious control over our usually occult inner body systems, a regulator or fine tuning mechanism for body processes. We ourselves emerge from the constricting forces of neurotic and inappropriate habit patterns and compelling inner forces and begin to enjoy a more creative and spontaneous life, one which is in tune with the solar rhythms of nature.

*1. W. Romanowski, 'The Role of Controlled Biological Rhythms in Modern Psycho-physical Education', *Fiep Bulletin*, Vol. 42, 1972 (Jan.–March), p. 62-66.

Therapeutic Principles

Surya namaskara is a versatile, adaptable and powerful tool in the yoga therapist's armament. It has a wide range of therapeutic applications. Because it is easy and enjoyable to perform and does not require a great deal of time, there is also good patient compliance.

In the previous chapters we have seen how surya namaskara revitalizes the physical organism and helps to maintain a dynamic and active lifestyle amidst the tensions and demands of our modern lifestyle. Good physical health is a prerequisite for good mental health. This is all part of surya namaskara's role as a preventative measure. We must not forget this most important aspect as prevention is far superior to cure.

In this section we will outline surya namaskara's therapeutic properties, describing how it attacks the disease process and helps to align physical function, energy flow and mental balance. Indeed, surya namaskara's role in mental health is far greater than most people suspect and in certain conditions, notably psychosis, it is one of the most useful and powerful tools the yoga therapist has at his disposal. In some situations it surpasses even meditation in its ability to rearrange the energies that, having become distorted, have led to varying degrees of mental and nervous breakdown.

Though surya namaskara is an efficient way to root out certain diseases, especially low energy disease states, psychosomatic and certain degenerative conditions, it must be used judiciously and wisely. Once again, of course, it should only be taught in a therapeutic setting under expert guidance. For this practice releases vast quantities of pranic flow that may have been trapped for many years.

The healing process must be slow and controlled if it is not to degenerate and result in more pain and discomfort in the form of healing crises, for example, boils, rashes, colds or diarrhea. In an even more extreme situation such as high blood pressure, stroke, coronary artery disease, hernia, intestinal tuberculosis or in a very debilitated body system, the extra energy released may be all that is required to tip the balance and destroy vital body organs. A pipe with a crack in it must be welded first before it can handle extra internal pressure. In the same way the healing process must be conducted in a stepwise and systematic way. This requires experience.

As a rule, all therapy should be undertaken under the guidance of a qualified medical practitioner and an expert yogic therapist.

Some disorders amenable to surya namaskara

A list of some of the disorders amenable to surya namaskara runs as follows: acne, boils, anemia, poor appetite, fatigue, obesity, underdevelopment, varicose veins, joint and rheumatic conditions, headache, asthma and other lung conditions, digestive upsets, indigestion, constipation, kidney problems, sluggish liver, low blood pressure, epilepsy, diabetes, skin conditions (eczema, psoriasis, leucoderma), prevention of the common cold, endocrine gland imbalance, menstrual and menopausal problems, mental conditions such as anxiety, depression, neurosis, psychosis, to name a few. It is also, of course, usual for generalized body development and to stimulate normal growth.

The basis of therapy

The human body is composed of a number of different organ systems working together to perform particular body functions and to maintain the organism as a whole. The vital processes, such as digestion, circulation of blood, etc., are not carried out in isolation, but result from the balanced interaction of various mutually interdependent organ systems. Failure of one system, organ or function has a detrimental effect on the whole body, disease is inevitable.

There are many reasons for the body systems to break down. Medical science knows of: congenital (from birth), infective, neoplastic (cancer), traumatic, metabolic, allergic, iatrogenic (doctor-induced), drug-induced, endocrine and neurological causes. There is also a large psychosomatic group, where the mind causes physical alterations and diseases. Despite this large variety of possible causes of disease, there is a large group of idiopathic or unknown causes.

From the yogic point of view, ill health is a result of an imbalance in the energy systems of the body. No matter how intelligent, or how good and law abiding a person may be, if his energy systems are not functioning properly, that person will suffer from disease. Often, a disease may strike without warning, however, it is more than likely that it has been latent for many years, buried in the genetic structure of the body or in some deep and subconscious area of the mind. A cure from disease, therefore, no matter what its apparent, surface causative factor, lies in the rebalancing of the energy systems which govern that area of body or mind and which are responsible for the maintenance of healthy growth, input and output, and so on. In this regard we have to study the flows of energy called ida and pingala.

Imbalance in the nadis

For most of us, total health, which ultimately leads to spiritual awakening, cannot be obtained. We constantly experience a fluctuation of energies, moods, periods of health and ill health, and the general ups and downs of life. This is the normal life process and is explained in yogic terms by the continual shift of energies from ida to pingala and back again in an approximately 90 minute cycle. The normal individual becomes ida predominant for 90 minutes and pingala predominant for

59

90 minutes. We are rarely in the balanced, sattwic state for more than a few minutes at a time. The balance occurs at the crossover point of each cycle.

A disease situation arises when an extreme shift in energy occurs outside of the normal range of flux experienced by relatively healthy individuals, or if the rhythm of shift is broken. For example, if we dwell excessively on our thoughts or on some event in our life, we evoke a continuous stream of mental energy which may be inappropriate. This is a neurotic situation. An extreme accentuation of internal mental pressures can cause an already imbalanced or weakened mind to break; the psychotic situation.

It is possible through our lifestyle to live in a predominantly pingala, extrovert, existence or in a predominantly ida, introvert existence. Though there is no extreme or acute stress, this situation invokes a generalized, chronic and weakening imbalance which can eventually lead to an acute breakdown and the manifestation of true illness later in life. At the same time, such imbalance is detrimental and not conducive to a happy existence.

1. *The pingala dominant individual:* A person who is mainly extrovert has very little access to internal experience, seeking to fill the inner void with external pleasures, desires and ambitions. Constantly grabbing outward for external securities and happiness cannot satisfy the inner needs. This leads to more frustrations and inner tensions which motivate more outward seeking behavior. Such pingala dominant individuals tend to overactivate their sympathetic nervous system, secreting too much acid and causing ulcers, producing angina pectoris or raising blood pressure beyond normal limits. They are constantly in a state of preparation for 'fight or flight', secreting too much adrenaline and performing too little exercise in order to burn up the excessive chemical secretions. Diseases manifest from the imbalance of endocrine secretions and metabolic processes. Such individuals may be restless and irritable, suffering 'dis-ease' in interpersonal situations.

2. *The ida dominant individual:* A person who is predominantly introverted by nature is a daydreamer who thinks a lot but

60

does not act on his thoughts. Such an individual is acutely aware of his feelings and usually oversensitive to outer events and interpersonal experiences. He may think of catastrophes and usually has little perspective on reality. There is little inner happiness due to a generalized inability 'to get things together' on the outside. These people are rarely active, physical types. They do not have enough vital energy to act efficiently in the world so as to carry out their plans, though, of course, the less severely imbalanced may get out and attempt many things. In an extreme case, physical vitality is very low and diseases such as constipation, depression, anxiety, ulcerative colitis, eczema, and a host of psychosomatic conditions develop in this climate.

Therefore we see two main patterns of disease:

1. *High physical energy diseases*, usually pingala predominant, a rajasic or dynamic state.
2. *Low physical energy diseases*, usually ida predominant, a tamasic or passive state.

Rebalancing the nadis

Low physical energy states are especially amenable to the practice of surya namaskara, this is because these conditions require a boost of prana shakti in order to develop the necessary physical stamina to overcome disease, and also to activate the catabolic processes of our metabolism so as to eliminate the buildup of excess waste products and hormones, such as adrenaline. Or we may want to speed up the metabolic rate. It is this dual aspect of surya namaskara, not only to squeeze chemicals out of body tissues, but to actually stimulate the very inter and intracellular energizing processes, that makes it such a powerfully therapeutic practice.

It is important in the low physical energy states to divert energy from mental activity to the physical plane by placing our awareness on the physical processes. We must not only activate the body and pingala nadi but we must focus our attention and mental energies upon the physical aspect, so as to reduce the mental input. This leads to rebalance.

One of the paradoxes of the therapeutic situation is that in low energy disease states, though our ultimate aim is to energize the body and reduce dissipation of mental energies, we initially tire the body. It requires some effort to perform a dynamic series of asanas, especially when body energy is low anyway. It is as though we are trying to turn a rusty wheel. Initially more effort is required. Once momentum has been achieved it becomes easier and easier, especially when we practise daily. The number of rounds should be increased slowly and progressively under guidance, to minimize strain.

The effect of tiring the body is twofold. The first is that we have less energy to think useless thoughts, to daydream of disasters or catastrophes, and to ruin our lives with unnecessary decisions. The second is that sleep comes more easily. Mental overactivity and physical underactivity prevent deep restful sleep, the kind of rest required for the regeneration of diseased tissues. Without proper sleep it is almost impossible to recover completely from any kind of chronic illness. This is one of the secrets of overcoming mild or acute psychotic episodes, for although the disease is mental, the brain requires deep sleep for rejuvenation.

In high physical energy disease states, we have to be very careful in using surya namaskara. An example of one of the few areas where it can be used in front line primary care is for low levels of increased high blood pressure. In these situations we have to maintain bodily fitness, however, not at the expense of damaged tissues. Other milder yogic practices, such as pawanmuktasana play a much more vital role.

Of course, in pingala-predominance, a reasonably healthy individual who uses surya namaskara will find that the quantity of his excessive energies is reduced by the practice, burnt up. This especially occurs when we speed up our practice. In fact this reduction of excess energy is actually a healthy state, developing from the rechannelling of blocked energy which has led to pingala predominance in the first place. Due to this process of regulation, the physical and mental energies are brought more into line and a better quality of energy is made available. At the same time the body becomes more flexible and we have more control over the nervous system, endowing us with greater sensitivity and skill. It is only in the diseased pingala-dominant state that we have to exercise extreme caution.

Surya namaskara in therapy

In the final analysis we see that surya namaskara acts to rebalance the energies of mind and body, depending on how we perform it. This knowledge allows us to modulate our body's energies according to need.

It is important for anyone practising surya namaskara, but especially so in therapy, to perform each stage of the practice accurately before moving on to the next. In the therapeutic situation it is rarely necessary to progress onto chakra awareness or mantra repetition. These constitute the spiritual side that we undertake when our body is healed and strengthened by asana and pranayama.

When practising surya namaskara for its therapeutic benefits it is wise to proceed slowly, whether pingala or ida is predominant. In this situation we may take 2, 3 or even more breaths during each asana, co-ordinating movement with breath, taking our time to develop awareness of the body and its limitations and the effects of breath on its inner functioning. An ida dominant individual would then aim to slowly increase the number of rounds and speed them up. A pingala dominant type would aim at maintaining or even slowing his practice and doing only a few rounds. Once his health returns he would speed up his practise. Once again, guidance, preferably in an ashram environment, is essential if the body is to once again function like a well-tuned machine.

Interaction with the Vital Organs

Though surya namaskara's ability to modulate intracellular and metabolic energy is perhaps its most remarkable and powerful feature, it also interacts with the physical organs of the body directly, applying pressure, massaging, stretching and generally toning up and supporting internal tissue structures. This aids the eliminative functions as well as stimulating nervous energy. It enhances our wellbeing.

The following is a systematic description of the benefits and effects of surya namaskara on each of the individual organ systems, so that the lay reader can better understand the effects on the various diseases pertaining to each.

Respiratory system

The lungs are made up of lobes, or compartments. In normal breathing one rarely utilizes all the lung compartments. Usually, only the lower portions are used while the upper areas collapse or may even become full of stagnant deposits of used air, carbon dioxide and toxic gases, especially in the case of city dwellers and smokers. These deposits remain in the lungs for years, adversely affecting respiration and other body systems.

In surya namaskara a deep rhythmic breathing process is synchronized with each movement which completely empties the lungs of all traces of stale gas and refills them with fresh, clean, oxygenated air. This is especially so with hasta uttanasana which maximally expands the chest wall. Padahastasana, when performed with mildly forced exhalation, which can be done with the mouth open, is a potent cleansing breath. All the pockets of the lungs are expanded, stimulated and then cleansed. The oxygen content of the blood is increased, which improves the overall vitality and oxygenation of the cells and tissues of the body and brain. Sluggishness and lethargy are rapidly overcome. Respiratory diseases and excess of mucus in the air passages can be eliminated. This practice is also good for the prevention of diseases such as tuberculosis, which develop in the little used, stagnant regions of the lungs.

Circulatory system

The practice of surya namaskara improves the heart action, but without strain, as is the case with body building or gymnastic exercises. The resultant increased flow of blood speeds up the elimination of waste matter and introduces fresh oxygen and nutrients to all the cells. Deposits of stagnant blood in the spleen and all other organs are removed, and general circulation is improved. The cardiac muscles are strengthened and the blood vessels of the heart, the coronary arteries, are stimulated to multiply, improving circulation and reducing the chance of heart attack. Sluggish circulation, cold hands and feet, blood vessel diseases and general fatigue can also be eliminated.

The circulation of lymph, which is of prime importance in fluid balance and in combatting infections, is toned. The body gains an increased resistance to infections, and a better ability to heal.

The enhanced feelings of wellbeing and the decreased effects of stress induced by surya namaskara reduce platelet stickiness. This, combined with better circulation ensure less likelihood of arteriosclerosis and many of the diseases which this produces, for example, coronary artery disease, heart attack, senility, renal impairment, reduced blood flow to the limbs necessitating amputation, and so on.

Padahastasana and parvatasana aid return of blood from the lower body to the heart, stretching leg muscles and using the force of gravity in the inverted position. The other asanas squeeze blood out of organs and aid the exchange of oxygen and food for waste products at the cell-blood vessel wall junction.

Digestive system

The alternate stretching and compressing movements of surya namaskara tone the whole digestive system by thoroughly massaging all the abdominal viscera. Padahastasana and bhujangasana are especially powerful in terms of compression and stimulating the abdominal organs. This not only enhances elimination but also increases the digestive fire, promoting a healthy appetite, and complete and rapid assimilation of food. Proper digestion is a prime factor in overall health. The quality or quantity of food matter little if the body is unable to digest, assimilate and utilize it efficiently. Undigested food ferments in the stomach and intestines creating gas, blocking the channels of elimination and the entire body. Digestive problems such as constipation, indigestion, diarrhea and sluggish liver can be relieved and prevented by dietary regulation in combination with yoga.

Urinary system

The kidneys perform the vital function of regulating water and salts in the body. They also strain impurities from the blood and excrete them in urine via the bladder. Any disruption in the normal kidney action results in rapid salt imbalance and increased blood nitrogen levels resulting in severe illness. Through the practice of surya namaskara, the spine and muscles of the back are exercised in such a way as to press and gently massage the kidneys. This stimulates their action and increases the flow of blood through them. If the kidneys are sluggish or in mild renal impairment, tendency to form stones or predisposition to infections characterized by dark, strong smelling urine, frequent urination and pain in the kidneys, it is suggested that one increases the intake of fresh water, as

66

well as taking a glass of water before practising gentle surya namaskara. Bhujangasana, ashtanga namaskara and ashwa sanchalanasana exert an especially strong influence on the kidney area.

Skin

The skin is the largest body organ and apart from holding the body together serves to regulate body temperature, as well as excreting quantities of waste matter through perspiration. When there is an excess of poisonous matter in the blood, it comes out through the skin in the form of boils, rashes and pimples. As surya namaskara produces perspiration, speeds up circulation and enhances the elimination of wastes through the digestive and urinary systems, it cleanses and endows the practitioner with a clean, glowing complexion which is an important sign of health. Many skin diseases caused by subcutaneous toxin deposits, such as pimples and eczema, can be removed. Bad odors from the body are eliminated, and the overall circulation of blood to the skin is improved.

When surya namaskara is practised in the early morning hours while facing the rising sun, ultraviolet light rays are absorbed through the skin. At sunrise, these rays are at their greatest intensity and are thought to be very beneficial for health as well as being responsible for vitamin D production. All the asanas stretch the skin and its elastic tissues, toning it and helping to preserve its functions.

Nervous system

In the twelve movements of surya namaskara, the spinal column is systematically stretched and compressed to the maximum extent, stimulating circulation in the whole spinal cord, and all nerve plexuses.

The peripheral nervous system, that which lies outside the central nervous system (brain and spine), consists of two parts, voluntary and involuntary. The voluntary system, or somato-motor system, governs the functions of the body which are under conscious control, such as major muscular movements. The involuntary system, or autonomic nervous system, governs those functions over which man gererally has no conscious control. Heartbeat, respiration, glandular secretions and functions of almost all internal organs are regulated according to the body's needs by impulses along the involuntary nerves. The involuntary system consists of two opposing subsystems: sympathetic and parasympathetic. Their balanced interaction maintains sound health. There is a tendency in modern man, however, for nervous functions to become imbalanced and to work disharmoniously.

Surya namaskara tones nerve flows by stimulating internal organs, which can be compared to the flowers at the end of the stem (nerve) of the plant. It stretches nerves, works on the spine and enhances prana which activates brain centers. After practising you may feel your body tingling with energy. The whole nervous system is activated and seems to wake up.

The Endocrine System

The endocrine glands are the most vital and mysterious of all systems. They play an overall role in the coordination and integration of all physiological processes and yet very little is actually known about them. The main function of the endocrine glands is the production and secretion of hormones, chemical substances released into the bloodstream and carried throughout the body to act upon particular organs. These hormones act as the mobilizers, stimulating the other organs to perform their respective functions. The following is a brief account of the glands and the beneficial effects of surya namaskara on their functions and malfunctions.

Pituitary

The pituitary gland is known as the body's master gland. This important center regulates the functions of the other glands, stimulating or inhibiting their secretions as the body requires. It has many hormonal secretions, which control the body's growth and development. By increasing the flow of blood to the head and through its effects on the nervous system, surya namaskara stimulates the hypothalamus which regulates the pituitary action. The practice of surya namaskara thereby has a direct and beneficial effect on this vital center and the whole body. The inverted asanas exert the most powerful effect on the pituitary gland.

69

Pineal

The pineal gland is a tiny gland in the brain. Yogic science states that it has a vital function as a connecting link between the different levels of awareness above and beyond the physical plane. Through stimulation of this center, one is able to contact the deeper layers of the mind and develop the powers of increased awareness, intuition, visualization and imagination which are inherent in every man. The pineal gland is known as the third eye. The inverted asanas are, again, foremost in toning this organ.

In children this center is very active, for children work mainly on the level of intuition and spontaneous awareness. Up to the age of seven a child forms the mental patterns which he will keep for the rest of his life, but as the child grows up, the ego and intellect begin to dominate his personality. The pineal gland atrophies from the age of eight years. Surya namaskara plays an important role in the maintenance of this important gland which acts as a window to man's higher psychic faculties.

Thyroid/parathyroid

The thyroid gland, located in the throat, controls the rate of metabolism or the speed at which the ingested food is burned by the body. Body heat, growth and development are also regulated by the secretions of this gland. The conditions of underactive thyroid (hypothyroid) results in the general slowing down of all bodily processes. The person becomes obese, lethargic, dull, feels perpetually cold and suffers from constipation and low blood pressure, and in extreme cases, arrested mental development. The opposite condition (hyperthyroid) is characterized by an exaggerated speeding up of all functions. The person eats more but loses weight and always feels hungry. He is nervous, excitable, oversensitive, sufferes from high blood pressure, and in extreme cases from nervous disorders with such symptoms as hallucinations, spasms, fits and protuding eyeballs. Disturbances of the thyroid are really more common than most people suspect, especially in women. Many people suffer from mild thyroid malfunction which is within normal limits but disturbs their everyday life. They suffer discomfort rather than disease. These are people who especially benefit from surya namaskara. Unfortunately, most people are not aware of the source of their problem or that the condition can be brought under control by the asanas. In the movements the throat area is alternatively pressed and then stretched, stimulating normal and balanced secretions of this vital gland which is linked to vishuddhi chakra.

The parathyroid glands are concerned with the metabolism of calcium and phosphorus, which are necessary for the development of strong, healthy bones. Overactivity causes brittle bones which break easily. The opposite condition produces tentany (muscular spasms and twitches) resulting from lack of calcium. In our experience, the practice of surya namaskara helps to normalize the function of the para-thyroids. Hasta uttanasana, parvatasana, bhujangasana and ashwa sanchalanasana exert more powerful effects on the neck.

Thymus

The thymus gland lies just below the thyroid, extending from the notch above the chest wall down into the chest. The thymus is larger in children and shrinks in size, and presumably in function, progressively with age. It is concerned with the production of antibodies which act as a defence against bacteria, viruses and other foreign invaders and against cancers which develop inside ourselves. This gland is concerned, therefore, with our relationship with the world.

In pranamasana we send prana to anahata chakra whose physical correlate is the thymus. Exhalation indicates giving to the world and at the same time the posture is introspective, indicative of looking within to improve ourselves. This mental attitude can beneficially stimulate and activate the thymus via anahata chakra.

Adrenal glands

The adrenal glands are two small bodies lying on top of the kidneys, which secrete a number of different hormones, most notably adrenalin. When a human being or animal is faced

71

with a situation of danger or great stress, large amounts of adrenalin are released into the blood to help him cope with the emergency. It acts immediately on almost all the vital functions, speeding up the heart and respiration, increasing the blood pressure, tensing all skeletal muscles, shutting down digestion, dilating the pupils of the eyes, causing the hair to stand on end, etc.

You may have had the experience of a sudden fright. At that time, as well as a feeling of shock radiating from the center of the abdomen, you would have experienced that for some time afterward a feeling of alertness and tenseness remained. This is due to the action of adrenalin. Overproduction of this hormone causes a person to be constantly in a state of nervous tension and anxiety, though he may be unaware of why he feels as he does. This is an especially common condition in today's stressful living conditions where we continually have to adapt to change. On the other hand, reduced production and secretion causes general dullness and failure to react to outer stimuli. The adrenal glands also play a part in sex hormone production and salt metabolism.

The positions of surya namaskara which apply direct pressure on the middle back region, where the kidneys and adrenal glands are located, massage and tend to correct imbalanced secretions, helping the adrenals to function optimally. The adrenals are linked to manipura chakra.

Pancreas

The pancreas is located behind the stomach at the level of the solar plexus. Parts of this important gland produce the hormone insulin, which controls the body's ability to store and utlize sugar. Insufficient production of insulin results in the inability of the body to use ingested sugar, causing excessive amounts to be released into the blood and also passed out with the urine. This dangerous and widespread disease is known as diabetes.

Surya namaskara compresses the abdominal organs which press onto the pancreas especially during backward bending in bhujangasana.

Reproductive organs

The reproductive glands regulate the production of sperm and ova, the develpoment of secondary sexual characteristics, such as hair growth, voice development, etc., plus the female menstrual cycle and development of breasts.

Surya namaskara is a valuable exercise for toning and regulating both male and female reproductive systems. In women the ovaries lie inside the abdomen and are stimulated more than in the male, helping to correct menstrual irregularities and the unnatural pains of premenstrual tension. The supporting muscles of the uterus and vaginal walls are strengthened. This also facilitates easy and painless childbirth. Asanas such as bhujangasana, padahastasana and ashwa sanchalanasana especially tone this area. Male sexual function is also improved by the stretch given in ashwa sanchalanasana.

Summary

These benefits of surya namaskara are based on observations gathered over the years in hundreds of students of all ages and origins who have come to our ashrams for training in yoga. Though surya namaskara does exert pressures on individual glands and organs, health comes from total body harmony and so, its therapeutic effects must be seen in a broader perspective.

The therapeutic effects given here are necessarily simplistic and mechanistic. A fuller explanation with scientific references and experimental data would be voluminous. The purpose of this text is to broaden the understanding of how surya namaskara works, especially in a therapeutic situation. This is important for teachers and therapists. It also helps to improve the practice. It is a good idea to study a book on anatomy and physiology so as to get a visual image of how the body works. This also helps enhance our body awareness and leads to better health.

Spinal Manipulation

All of the movements of surya namaskara are generated around forward and backward bending of the spinal column. This alternate flexing of the spine gives innumerable benefits to the body, rarely matched by other forms of physical development. All yoga asanas recognize the importance of a healthy, strong and flexible spine in the quest for overall health. However, its importance extends beyond this. The spinal passageway is the conducting path for sushumna, the central nadi through which the awakened and liberated shakti passes during its ascent to sahasrara.

A deeper understanding of the spine's structure and function will enable us to appreciate more fully the importance of surya namaskara, not only for purposes of physical health, but also in relation to the process of spiritual awakening.

Structure and function

The spinal column is constructed of 33 vertebrae, stacked one on top of the other in a gentle S-shaped curve. The frontal part of each vertebra is round and flat on the top and bottom. These flat portions fit on top of each other, separated by a spongy pad or disc. This acts as a shock absorber between each vertebra, while keeping them slightly separated. The rear portion of the spinal column is hollow, and contains all the nerves conducted from the brain to the various organs in

74

the body. These nerves then branch out to their respective organs through the spaces between each vertebra. The whole structure is maintained in place by a complex arrangement of muscles, tendons and ligaments.

The spine is like the trunk of a tree, supporting the entire body structure. On top of this trunk sits the bony, enclosed cranium, or box of the skull, containing the most important of all human organs— the brain. The topmost vertebra is called the atlas because it supports the head like the mythical Greek figure, Atlas, who supported the earth upon his shoulders. The second vertebra is the peg-like axis, so named because the atlas and skull rotate upon it. Thus the head can move independently, or with the neck.

In the thoracic region, the spine supports the expansive ribcage, composed of the rib bones, muscles and cartilage. Moving further down, in the lumbar or abdominal region, the spinal column is an anchor for the muscles which hold the gastrointestinal organs in place. These are held suspended as if in a cloth handbag with the spine forming the handle.

At the lower (sacral) end of the spine is the pelvis which is like a bony basket cradling the excretory and reproductive organs. The five sacral vertebrae are used to form a single bone at the back of the pelvis. These are smaller, as they have no actual weight bearing function, and take no part in the movements of the spine. At the very end of these sacral vertebrae is the vestigial tail, the coccyx.

The spine is not absolutely erect in the true sense but has four distinct curves. The cervical (neck) curve has 7 vertebrae, the dorsal (chest) curve has 12, the lumbar (lower back) curve has 5 and the sacral (pelvic) curve also has 5. Each vertebra progressively bears the weight of the column. Thus each lower vertebra is slightly larger than the one above, in order to bear the increasing load. The atlas, for example, is only one quarter as large as the lumbar vertebra.

Due to this intricate structure, the spine is capable of performing a wide variety of movements. It can bend forwards, backwards, sideways, and twist. This gives the body a great deal of freedom of movement in performing its various tasks.

Evolutionary development

Back problems can largely be related to an evolutionary inconsistency which occurred during man's progression from quadruped to biped. Structurally, the spine is designed like a suspension bridge, supported at each end. Originally it was intended for operation in the horizontal position, i.e. when we moved about on four legs. However, at some period of development, man began to stand upright, walking on two legs, and the problems began. Of course, this does not mean to say that other compensatory changes have not occurred during the course of evolution, but this basic inconsistency of evolutionary development remains at the root cause of the complex problems that can manifest from the spine.

The supportive muscular development that proceeded in compensation for the spine's vertical operation is sufficient to ensure proper support for the vertebrae, and consequently the rest of the body. However, inaequate exercise of this musculature, obesity and poor posture, such as occur with continual forward bending during working activities or due to chairs, are responsible for the majority of the spinal disorders which appear in man today.

Common spinal disorders

It should be understood that in relation to spinal problems, surya namaskara is best used as a preventive measure. Although it may overcome many back problems once they have developed, in some of the cases discussed below, a program of other asanas would be more suitable initially. However, regular practise of surya namaskara can prevent these problems by mobilizing the intervertebral joints, developing the supportive musculature of the spine, strengthening the ligaments, and massaging the nerves and blood vessels. This becomes even more important in middle and later life, when the muscles tend to become weaker and the spine stiffer.

The most troublesome area of the spine is the lumbar (lower back) region. Its problems are manifold. The paravertebral muscles become stiff and painful with the buildup of emotional, sexual and menstrual tensions. They sprain by inco-ordinate actions while lifting, bending or driving. Spinal ligaments are torn by hard pulls or blows received during sports, etc. The muscles are imbalanced if the body weight is not equally divided between both legs, due to some disease of the lower limbs. Probably, the most common causes of lower back pain, however, are due to poor posture, lack of exercise and sedentary life.

In an obese person, extra strain is placed on the lumbar region due to the extra weight of fat deposits in the mesentry of the intestines, or the abdominal wall. Stretching of ligaments occurs and weaknesses appear. This is because, as a rule, obese people eat too much and do not get enough exercise.

Slipped disc and sciatica are caused when the cartilaginous ring of the shock absorbing spinal discs ruptures and creates pressure on the nerves between the vertebrae. This is excruciatingly painful. If the spinal discs degenerate, friction from one vertebra moving against the other can cause further wear and degeneration of the vertebrae along with a great deal of pain.

In cases of slipped disc, sciatica, and disc degeneration, the forward bending postures of surya namaskara will aggravate the problem. Therefore, all forward bending postures should be avoided in these cases, and a guided program of backward bending asanas is recommended.

Headaches, due to mental and postural tensions, occur when the muscles of the head, neck or shoulders become tightened and spasmed. The spasms can be felt as tender, hard cords or knots. Deep emotional tensions can also cause muscular spasm and pain in the thoracic region, which is often difficult to alleviate due to the bracing effect of the ribcage. The alternating movements of surya namaskara can be extremely useful in loosening these areas of the chest, neck and shoulders, preventing the buildup of muscle tension where spasm occurs.

Scoliosis is a condition which occurs when the spine develops a sideways curvature. It is often an S-shaped curve, as one end of the spine moves in compensation for misalignment at the other end. It can be caused by hip displacement, unequal muscle tension in each side of the back, or imbalanced growth of the muscular and skeletal systems during early teens. In this case, the backward bending postures should be minimized and forward stretches accentuated to pull the spine straight.

Spinal problems are complex and numerous, however, regular practice of surya namaskara under expert guidance will improve the condition of the spine, and ensure a lifetime free from back problems.

To fully complement the range of spinal movements, in a non-therapeutic situation, sideways bending asanas such as tiryaka tadasana and the trikonasana series, along with spinal twists such as ardha matsyendrasana can be incorported into the daily practice program. Then the complete range of forward, backward, sideways and twisting motions of the spine are completed.

Sushumna

The radical evolutionary step of becoming upright separates man from other animals, giving him a distinct advantage over them. This also applies to his spiritual evolution as well. Some interesting points are worth noting in this context.

Firstly, it is said that only through human incarnation can a being attain enlightenment, it is not possible in an animal incarnation.

Secondly, within the spinal column is sushumna passage, which contains the physical location points of the chakras, the psychic centers that govern man's development of higher awareness and override his animal tendencies. The lowest of these chakras, mooladhara, which governs the most basic and instinctive aspects of our nature is located at the base of the spine, not actually in the spinal cord itself. As we move up sushumna, the chakras express higher and more refined qualities, which eventually transcend the mundane nature of humanity. Each higher chakra involves progressively more complicated neural structures.

On the physical level, the passage of nerve energy requires keeping the spinal column free from obstructions, so that the impulses from the brain can be transmitted to the rest of the body, and vice versa. This in turn is reflected in the psychic body, ensuring that the awakened kundalini has a clear passageway in its ascent to the brain.

Thus, the manipulation which surya namaskara gives to the whole of the spinal column does more than maintain structural stability in the body. It also represents a purification of the vital sushumna passage so that our energies can ascend from the root of our lower nature to awaken our highest faculties.

Effects on the Muscles

The following chapter gives an account of the effects of surya namaskara on the muscles of the body, the majority of which are exercised. This chapter is intended especially for yoga teachers and therapists, as a guide for developing better technique and physique. It is also intended for the individual who wants to understand just what he is doing to himself in a purely physical sense and thereby improve his practice through awareness of just which muscle he is supposed to relax, tense or stretch.

Strength

It is important to remember that surya namaskara does not seek to develop hypertrophied, overdeveloped muscles. Rather it is designed to stretch, tone and realign the musculo-skeletal structures, slowly reinforcing better posture and health and reintegrating better total body function through this realignment. We must see our muscles in perspective, in harmonious interrelationship with other body organs.

Each muscle is composed of a number of fibers and each fiber is composed of sliding segments which fit into one another in much the same way as a slide rule, or sliding door. There is a certain alignment of fibers which allows optimal efficiency. If the resting position is moved in either direction from the optimum alignment, the force each fiber can contribute to the whole muscle is diminished. Strength is not so much a function of muscle bulk, but is more a consequence of the consolidation and concerted, co-ordinated effort of the individual fibers within the muscle. If there is excessive tension, the muscle fibers do not lengthen enough and strength is then a function of the number of fibers rather than coordination. This is usually the situation with body builders. If the fibers of the muscle are too long they may not function at all.

Balance

Gravity exerts a force on all material objects. Each part and segment of the human body has a gravitational center around which it functions. Each center of gravity also influences the overall center of gravity of the body. This center of gravity changes continuously according to the position of the body. In every position, whether lying, sitting, keeping an erect posture, or moving, the concept of balance is ever present. Physical balance can only be maintained if gravity is neutralized. This occurs through:
- the pressure of joint articulations against each other
- ligamentous resistance
- sustained muscular contractions coordinated by the sensory-motor nervous system.

The balance of the body improves as the area in contact with the ground increases because the center of gravity is lowered. Balance is not a static thing. It requires continuous adjustment in relation to our fluctuating posture, movements, breath cycle and level of awareness.

The cerebellum, at the back of the brain, plays an essential part in maintaining balance of the body. Here the auditory, visual, sensory and muscular inputs meet and are integrated to determine and maintain our ongoing postural status through continous feedback and reassessment at the unconscious, autonomic (vegetative) level of the nervous system.

Composure

In yoga, before moving into any new position, awareness of the starting position is of utmost importance. Composure is

81

as necessary here as it is before commencing any spiritual practice or important task. In pranamasana, for example, you should first become aware of the unceasing activity that the postural muscles are performing in order to maintain static balance. Give yourself an opportunity to develop awareness of this very subtle work. This develops a new and higher awareness that you can carry into the more dynamic postures. We must try to develop the delicate balance between muscular tension and relaxation.

PRANAMASANA

Pranamasana is a position of composure, tranquility and stability. It is a symbol of that stage in man's evolutionary development when he became upright and erect. Therefore, in pranamasana, we are concerned with the muscles responsible for maintaining an erect posture.

Other important muscles in which a resting tone is maintained in order to stand in pranamasana include:
— calves: soleus, tibialis anterior, popliteus
— thighs: adductors, hamstrings (biceps femoris, semi-tendinosus, semimembranosus)
— trunk: spinal and anterior abdominal muscles are essential
— scapular area: trapezius, rhomboid
— neck: anterior and posterior muscles are necessary to keep the neck in position and the head erect.

Erect posture
The muscles responsible for the erect posture hold the spine, maintain its curvatures, work the legs, and support the head.
1. *Feet and lower legs:* the muscles at the front of the lower legs, which extend, or raise the toes and move the foot upward, constantly adjust the center of gravity of the body so that it is brought forward onto the base. With eyes open, and then closed, place your awareness at this lowest adjusting point and experience the state of dynamic muscular equilibrium required to maintain balance.

2. *Hips:* the psoas muscles are most essential for bringing the spine to the upright human stance. Psoas joins the legs to the trunk, linking the transverse processes of the lumbar vertebrae to the lesser trochanter of the femur (upper and outer thigh bone) on each side. It is this muscle which gives the lower back its characteristic forward sway, bringing the center of gravity of the trunk forward, above and between the feet. Its function is to help the body to adjust its position in space. The psoas muscle constantly contracts and relaxes in order to adjust posture. It is involved in a dynamic process.

The action of the psoas is modified by the action of the diaphragm, a thin sheet of horizontal muscle responsible for breathing. The lower fibers of the diaphragm accentuate the sway of the lumbar spine (small of the back) in order to bring it forward. The diaphragm contracts with every breath and thereby affects the psoas, posture and balance. We can better understand how subtle and sensitive the control for these muscles regulating the body have to be. It is also easy to see that tension which prevents these muscles from acting fully, interferes with posture, creating excessive sway, frozen pelvis or other structural and ultimately functional disfunctions.

3. *Trunk:* quadratus lumborum originates from the iliac crest (hip) and the iliolumbar ligament (pelvic girdle) and is connected to the lowest rib and upper four lumbar vertebrae. It adjusts the center of gravity of the trunk on the legs.

4. *Spine:* the short and deep transversospinalis muscles running obliquely upwards and medially from the transverse processes to the spines of the vertebrae are the major postural muscles concerned with maintaining the vertebral column erect. They are supported by the intertransversari, small muscles between the transverse processes of the vertebrae and the interspinales, which are placed in pairs between the spines of contiguous vertebrae. In addition to this, the transversospinalis muscles pass on the nerve impulses to other postural muscles in front of and behind the spine to maintain the sustained muscular contraction which keeps the trunk erect and firm.

5. *Head:* held upright by splenius capitis, scalenus medius and scalenus posterior which bolster the back of the cervical spinal column, center the head on the trunk and enable the head to move back and forth.

These postural muscles, in the upright position, are worked throughout all the standing positions and will not be emphasized in discriptions of these asanas unless specifically worked on by the asana concerned.

Enhancing posture

To enhance our posture during pranamasana, try the following suggestions:

1. To reduce the sway at the small of the back, contract the gluteus muscles (buttocks) slightly while simultaneously holding the abdominal wall slightly contracted inwards. The transversus abdominis, the innermost flat muscle of the abdominal wall (extending between the iliac crest and the 12th rib and from the inner surfaces of the lower costal cartilages) acts on the abdominal contents. The pressure of the diaphragm and transversus abdominis will establish intra abdominal and intra thoracic pressure and, in the specific case of pranamasana, maintain the pelvis and lumbar region in the correct position.

2. To straighten the cervical region and increase height, bring the chin slightly toward the front of the neck without lowering the head. Here, it is the sternocleidomastoid muscles, originating from the sternum and clavicle, and inserting onto the mastoid portion of temporal bone behind the ears which do the work.

While stretching the head upward, feel the stretch on the rest of the spine and visualize energy flowing upward. This can be done at the same time as, or instead of anahata chakra awareness. It is this aspect of the practice which is a clear example of the most basic tantric principle, using the body to transcend the body. In pranamasana we can use muscle awareness and the stretching of the body to help consciousness ascend to higher levels. Pranamasana is much more than just standing with the hands in the prayer position.

HASTA UTTANASANA

In hasta uttanasana, positions 2 and 11 of surya namaskara, the practitioner opens himself and communicates with the immense potentiality and strength that the sun represents for man. This posture has long been a part of spiritual and occult traditions invoking the grace and power of higher forces. To open himself to the cosmic fire, the practitioner slightly pushes forward the solar plexus (manipura chakra), and, therefore the pelvis. The gravity center of the body thus comes further forward between the feet. Then, the arms are stretched upwards, coming into contact with the ears. The head bends back and looks upward, stretching the front and compressing the back of the neck.

The body experiences a complete anterior stretch and a slight posterior contraction, assuming a slight curve from feet to head, as though it were being stretched like a bow by powerful spiritual forces. Allow yourself to relax and bend with the posture. Push the chest a little forward aiming to straighten the curve of the upper back slightly. When performed in a relaxed manner, this aids in opening up to the cosmic, pranic and spiritual forces.

Maintenance of balance can be a little difficult in this posture as the action of raising the arms raises the center of gravity. Tension results from trying too hard to push the chest forward. Therefore, it should be performed gradually at first, increasing the forward curve as you adjust to the position. The following muscles are used to maintain this posture:
— Upper arm and shoulder: the muscles from scapula to humerus (the bony shaft of the upper arm) move the limb: the teres major and minor, deltoid, coracobrachialis. The latissimus dorsi, originating from the lower six thoracic vertebrae, sacrum, posterior part of crest of ilium and lower four ribs, and taking its insertion onto the humerus also extends the arm.
— Forearm: the triceps brachii extends the forearm.
— Wrist: the fingers and hands are also extended by palmaris brevis, tensing the palm, extensor digitorum communis

on the humerus and inserting on the back of each finger, extend the wrist and fingers, as does the extensor carpi ulnaris, extensor carpi radialis longus and brevis.
— Back: trapezius and latissimus dorsi are contracted with slight emphasis on the buttocks.
— Front: serratus anterior on the chest expands the rib cage and increases breathing capacity. Abdominal muscles are stretched, including rectus abdominis, a strap muscle in the center of the abdomen, running from the pubis up to the 5th, 6th and 7th ribs, external and internal oblique, transversus abdominis.

PADAHASTASANA

This pose is the complete opposite of position 2. From a powerful upward stretch we go into a powerful downward stretch. After having invoked divine forces man brings these to the earth by touching the ground and thereby transforming his earthly existence. Man surrenders to and consciously utilizes the force of gravity.

Padahastasana is a passive position in which the posterior muscles of the body receive a major stretch as the trunk folds on the legs. The hands, with palms flat, are placed beside the feet or even behind the body so as to stretch it still further. This time the anterior muscles are passively massaged. This is an inverted position, with swadhisthana chakra at the top. The following muscles are involved:
— Trunk: psoas and iliacus (originating from the iliac fossa to insert into the area of the psoas insertion) bend the trunk forward.
— Abdomen: muscles are relaxed.
— Neck: sternocleidomastoid and scalenus (from cervical vertebrae to first 2 ribs) bend the head forward.
— Back: stretching of paravertebral muscles, latissimus dorsi (lumbar and lower thoracic), ilocostalis (lumbar, thoracic and cervical), cervical spinalis and spinalis capitis (neck), trapezius, teres major, teres minor, infraspinatus.

- Arms: stretching of the arms and hands is as for hasta uttanasana, especially triceps.
- Buttocks: gluteus maximus and minimus are stretched.
- Legs: hamstrings at the back of the thighs, soleus and popliteus in the calves, and also extensors of the toes which aim to maintain posture, are all exercised.

ASHWA SANCHALANASANA

The practice of surya namaskara can be thought of as a way for the practitioner to develop his awareness of space. After measuring and exploring the space attained by means of the arms in position 2 and 3, the practitioner, from position 4 begins to explore space by extending one of his legs as far back as possible. The space between the separated feet constitutes the territory covered by an individual in surya namaskara and this space will be explored in the following positions. But first he should 'recognize' the space he can cover in position 4.

In this asymmetric posture, the main muscles used are those of the lower limbs. Though the center of gravity is lowered, balance is made more difficult because the base of the posture is not wide and the posture is asymmetrical. Placing the hands beside the feet enlarges the base and improves balance. The muscles used to extend the back and head backwards are the same as for hasta uttanasana, the main difference being that this movement is more pronounced and the arms are lowered to the ground.

Most of the stretch of this asana is on the front of the thighs, hips, abdominal muscles, and on the back and neck.

The following positions of the legs will be assumed:
- Front leg: dorsiflexion of ankle, flexion of knee, flexion of hip. Gluteus maximus and hamstrings are stretched. Other leg muscles are relaxed.
- Back leg: support on toes (extension), passive dorsiflexion of ankle, slight flexion of knee. Quadriceps femoris and psoas are stretched.

87

PARVATASANA

The mountain posture is, as one would expect from its name, a symmetrical, stable posture. It is a semi-inverted posture in which balance is attained by increasing the width of the base even further, by placing the second foot back.

The main stretch of this posture is in the back of the neck, upper back and back of the legs. The muscles involved in movement are in the arms, which are strengthened. The rest of the stretch is passive. The muscles stretched include:
- Calves: soleus, popliteus, achilles tendon (at the back of the ankle).
- Thighs: hamstrings. The buttocks are slightly stretched.
- Trunk: abdominal muscles are slightly tensed: the main back muscles involved are longissimus thoracis, trapezius, latissimus dorsi, teres major and minor (which are also involved in movement of the arms). The shoulder muscles are actively contracted while the arms are kept extended and straight.

ASHTANGA NAMASKARA

This is a position of surrender to earthly bondage and ties. The following muscles are involved:
- Ankles and toes: toes are passively extended, stretching extensor digitorum longus and extensor hallucis longus, ankles are passively extended, stretching tibialis anterior (upper tibia to inside of foot).
- Knees: the knees are flexed by the hamstrings at the back of the thigh.
- Upper leg: psoas major and iliacus flex the thigh while psoas minor flexes the trunk.
- Neck: is extended backward by longissimus cervicis (upper 4th and 5th thoracic vertebrae to 2nd to 6th cervical vertebrae, longissimus capitis (spreads from the occipital bone, 7th cervical to 12th thoracic vertebrae to scapula), is contracted. The front of the neck is stretched.

— Arms: trapezius is also involved in supporting the body as are rhomboid major and minor (upper part of the back).

BHUJANGASANA

Bhujangasana utilizes the backward bending muscles of the back to extend the spine and neck backwards. This movement is mainly performed by the hands and arms which push the relaxed body backward into a dynamic curve.

The main muscles involved are:
— Arms: triceps brachii– straighten the arms.
— Back: all the back muscles are compressed but not tensed in the final position.
— Abdomen: stretching of abdominal muscles occurs. The buttocks are also slightly contracted in order to maintain the legs together and still.
— Legs: hamstrings are flexed slightly in order to maintain leg position.

Developing the Practice

The seven basic asanas at the core of surya namaskara provide the basis for an integrated and complete practice. They are the basis for not only a beautiful series of postures but also are the seeds of a new and powerful experience of the physical organism.

The aim of the dynamic aspect of surya namaskara is to energize and harmonize the physical structure. When combined with breath and mantra it extends its effects into the more subtle bodies and areas of personality. As the practice slows down it becomes more subtle and we gain better understanding of the interaction of breath and nadis as well as body and mind. Awareness expands as the practice touches and awakens deeper areas of our personality.

Deepening of awareness requires the breaking down of our limitations. In effect we are exploring our physical posture as a doorway into new realms of experience and therefore must overcome certain obstacles within both the body and mind. Stiffness of the body is merely a reflection of mental stiffness, rigidity in thinking and lack of creativity. Habits concentrate posture and flows of energy into set patterns which enhance certain body organs and functions but neglect others. It is this over-energizing of some areas and under-energizing of others that leads to disease and it is this imbalance that surya namaskara seeks to rectify.

As we practise the series of 24 asanas we should aim at gradually and progressively increasing our awareness of each posture. We have to feel as though we are getting more deeply inside the body so as to recontact our physical dimension and also to become more aware of and breakdown our limitations. Why can't we do a certain posture? What is holding us back? Each obstacle we find must then be worked on slowly and steadily over a period of time. In this regard we can add other asanas into the series so that we enhance the effect of the practice on the body.

Sample Practice

The following routine is one example of how the series of asanas in surya namaskara can be extended so as to aid the development of awareness and flexibility (see Asana Pranayama Mudra Bandha, published by the Bihar School of Yoga, for details of asanas mentioned in this section). It can be practised before a dynamic series to limber up, or afterwards to aid awareness of prana.

Position 1: Pranamasana is a starting point for a meditative frame of mind during the practice. We should take time to develop awareness of breath, the position of the hands and the effect of this position on our feelings and attitudes.

Position 2: Hasta uttanasana allows us to raise energy in the frontal passage, extending from mooladhara up to bindu and moving along the front of the body. Once the energy is raised we can stretch into tadasana, or by raising one hand a little more and then the other, stretch the sides of the chest and waist. We can also perform tiryaka tadasana in this position.

Position 3: Padahastasana relies on the use of gravity to gradually stretch the back of the body. The action of gravity is intensified by placing the interlocked hands on the back of the head. In this position we can pull the elbows backward so as to pull on the muscles on the front of the chest. This is beneficial in asthma, for example. From this posture we can move into dwikonasana, with the interlocked hands stretched out behind. The effect of gravity is further enhanced and the muscles

91

of the shoulder girdle are relaxed and strengthened. Moving the arms from side to side stretches tension out of the shoulder girdle and provides a massage to the upper back, enhancing circulation. Another alternative is to move into samakonasana' a few times and then to flop back into padahastasana.

Position 4: Ashwa sanchalanasana provides the basis for asanas to strengthen the pelvis, hips, thighs and sense of balance. We can raise the hands up in the air, as for hasta uttanasana and thereby increase the stretch on the front of the extended leg and strengthen the thigh and hip of the bent leg. Alternatively we can place the interlocked hands behind the back, as for dwikonasana, so as to enhance the curve of the back and intensify the practice even more.

Position 5: Sumeru asana does not lend itself easily to many variations, however, by moving from one foot to the other we enhance the stretch on the back of the leg.

Position 6: Ashtanga namaskara is another practice which is difficult to vary. We should aim to bring the knees closer to the body to enhance the effect on the back.

Position 7: Bhujangasana is often difficult to perform early in the morning. When there is stiffness it is a good idea to perform positions 5, 6 and 7 dynamically a few times so as to loosen the back muscles. Tiryaka bhujangasana is also a very dynamic approach to loosening the back.

Expanding the experience
When we take our time and move through surya namaskara slowly, with awareness and control of breath we develop more understanding and knowledge of the body. One round may take 10, 15 or even 20 minutes to perform, however, in that time we can perform 50 asanas or more and can loosen almost the entire musculature as well as affecting the internal organs. At the same time we are not falling into the old habitual tendency of forming habits but are rather learning to creatively and intuitively flow with the needs of our body.

As we become accustomed to the joy and wellbeing of stretching, breathing and learning about the body, it becomes more and more difficult to develop the chronic tensions responsible for disease. The experience of exploring the body, releasing tension and feeling good is self-reinforcing and extends into the day no matter what activity we are performing or what position we are in. While sitting in a chair we can stretch our arms up or back, or while standing we can simply move into hasta uttanasana or fall forward into padahastasana to remove much of the fatigue and stiffness which develops during a busy day.

In this way we take the responsibility for our health and happiness into our own hands and are no longer at the mercy of restricting social conventions and external forces. We move outside set patterns of neurotic behavior and begin to dance through life with joy and spontaneity. We also affect our environment, for a relaxed and happy person infects the minds of others in a positive way. Though people may initially make jokes about anything out of the ordinary they soon become inquisitive, especially when faced with their own tensions, generated by modern living. This is how fads develop.

Developing the practice of surya namaskara can have repercussions on our whole lifestyle and attitude to life. The exploration of ourselves that we initiate in our daily practice expands in concentric circles out into our daily activity, movement, interaction with people and things and thus helps to change our lives in a positive and creative way.

Surya Namaskara in a Nutshell

Posture	Mantras	Concentration	Diagram
1. Pranamasana	Om mitraya namaha Om hram	Heart center Anahata	*Exhale*
2. Hasta uttanasana	Om ravaye namaha Om hrim	Neck center Vishuddhi	*Inhale*
3. Pada hastasana	Om suryaya namaha Om hroom	Root of spinal column Swadhisthana	*Exhale*
4. Ashwa sanchalan- asana	Om bhanave namaha Om hraim	Eyebrow center Ajna	*Inhale*

94

Posture	Mantras	Concentration	Diagram
5. Parvatasana	Om khagaya namaha *Om hraum*	Neck center Vishuddhi	 *Exhale*
6. Ashtanga namaskara	Om pushne namaha *Om hraha*	Behind navel Manipura	 *Retain*
7. Bhujangasana	Om hiranya-garbhaya namaha *Om hram*	Root of spinal column Swadhisthana	 *Inhale*
8. Parvatasana	Om marichaye namaha *Om hrim*	Neck center Vishuddhi	 *Exhale*
9. Ashwa sanchalan-asana	Om adityaya namaha *Om hroom*	Eyebrow center Ajna	 *Inhale*
10. Pada hastasana	Om savitre namaha *Om hraim*	Root of spinal column Swadhisthana	 *Exhale*

Posture	Mantras	Concentration	Diagram
11. Hasta uttanasana	Om arkaya namaha	Neck center Vishuddhi	
	Om hraum		*Inhale*
12. Pranamasana	Om bhas- karaya namaha	Heart center Anahata	
	Om hraha		*Exhale*

INTERNATIONAL YOGA FELLOWSHIP MOVEMENT

A charitable and philosophical movement founded by Paramahamsa Satyananda at Rajnandgaon in 1956 to disseminate the yogic tradition throughout the world.

Medium of conveying the teachings of Paramahamsa Satyananda through the affiliate centres around the world.

Paramahamsa Niranjanananda is the first Paramacharya of the International Yoga Fellowship Movement.

Provides guidance, systematised yoga training programme and sets teaching standards for all the affiliated yoga teachers, centres and ashrams.

A Yoga Charter to consolidate and unify the humanitarian efforts of all sannyasin disciples, yoga teachers, spiritual seekers and well-wishers was introduced during the World Yoga Convention in 1993.

Affiliation to this Yoga Charter enables the person to become a messenger of goodwill and peace to the world, through active involvement in various far-reaching yoga related projects.

BIHAR SCHOOL OF YOGA (BSY)

A charitable and educational institution founded by Paramahamsa Satyananda at Munger in 1963 to impart yogic training to all nationalities.

Paramahamsa Niranjanananda is the Chief Patron of BSY.

Focal point for a mass return to the ancient science of yoga.

The original school, Sivanandashram, is the centre for the Munger locality.

Ganga Darshan, the new school, established in 1981, is situated on a historical hill with a panoramic view of the Ganges.

Yoga Health Management, Teacher Training, Sadhana, Kriya Yoga and other specialised courses are held throughout the year. Renowned for its sannyasa training and the initiation of female and foreign sannyasins.

Provides trained sannyasins and teachers for conducting yoga conventions, seminars and lectures tours around the world.

Has a well-staffed research library and scientific research centre.

SIVANANDA MATH

A social and charitable institution founded by Paramahamsa Satyananda at Munger in 1984 in memory of Swami Sivananda Saraswati of Rishikesh.

Head Office now situated at Rikhia in Deoghar district, Bihar.

Paramahamsa Niranjanananda is the Chief Patron.

Aims to facilitate growth of the weaker and underprivileged sections of the society, especially the rural communities.

Activities include: distribution of free scholarships, clothing, farm animals and food; the digging of tube-wells and construction of houses for the needy; assistance to farmers in ploughing and watering their fields.

A small dispensary has been established for the provision of medicine, and veterinary services are also provided.

Tribhuvan Office, a three storey complex to deal with Sivananda Math's activities, will also house the satellite dish system for providing global information to the villagers.

All services are provided free and universally to everyone regardless of caste and creed.

YOGA RESEARCH FOUNDATION

A scientific, research-oriented institution founded by Paramahamsa Satyananda at Munger in 1984.

Paramahamsa Niranjanananda is the Chief Patron of the institute.

Aims to provide an accurate assessment of yoga practices within a scientific framework, and to establish yoga as an essential science for the development of mankind.

Conducted a symposium of over 100 medical professionals from India and abroad with a view to consolidating interest and work in yoga research and health investigation at Munger in 1988 and 1989.

At present conducting international research on the effects of yoga on respiratory disorders involving 10,000 subjects worldwide.

Future plans include literary, scriptural, medical and scientific investigations into other little-known aspects of yoga for physical health, mental wellbeing and spiritual upliftment.

SRI PANCHDASHNAM PARAMAHAMSA ALAKH BARA

Sri Panchdashnam Parama-hamsa Alakh Bara was established in 1990 by Paramahamsa Satyananda at Rikhia, Deoghar, Bihar. It is a charitable, educational and non-profit making institution.

Upholds and propagates the highest tradition of sannyasa, namely vairagya (dispassion), tyaga (renunciation) and tapasya (austerity). Propounds the tapovan style of living adopted by the rishis and munis of the vedic era and is intended only for sannyasins, renunciates, ascetics, tapasvis and paramahamsas.

Alakh Bara does not conduct any activities such as yoga teaching or preaching of any religion or religious concepts.

The guidelines set down for the Alakh Bara are based on the classical vedic tradition of sadhana, tapasya and swadhyaya or atma chintan.

Paramahamsa Satyananda, who now resides permanently at the Alakh Bara, performs the Panch-agni Vidya and other vedic sadhanas, thus paving the way for future paramahamsas to uphold their tradition.

BIHAR YOGA BHARATI (BYB)

The Bihar Yoga Bharati Institute was founded by Parama-hamsa Niranjanananda in 1994 as an educational and charitable institution for advanced studies in yogic sciences.

It is the culmination of the vision of Swami Sivananda Saraswati and Paramahamsa Satyananda.

BYB is the first institute in the world of its kind to impart comprehensive yogic education with provisions to grant higher degrees in yogic studies such as MA, MSc, MPhil, DLit, and PhD to the students.

It offers a complete scientific, yogic education and training according to the need of the present times, through the Faculties of Yoga Philosophy, Yoga Psychology and Applied Yogic Science.

Residential courses of three months to two years are conducted in a Gurukula environment, so that along with yoga education, the spirit of seva (selfless service), samarpan (dedication) and karuna (compassion) for humankind is also imbibed by the students.